Geology
and
Creation

100 Questions and Answers
from a Biblical Perspective

Don DeYoung

Creation Research Society
Reader Series: Number 5

Creation Research Society Books

Geology and Creation
100 Questions and Answers from a Biblical Perspective

Don DeYoung

ISBN: 0-940384-29-9

Printed in the United States of America

Dedication

This book is dedicated to my three sons-in-law, Gene O'Hara, Scot Bail, and Derrik Hobbs. Together we have backpacked to mountain heights and canyon depths.

Table of Contents

Introduction

Many people misunderstand the word *creation* in the title of this book. At first it may sound like an outdated idea from the distant past. After all, this is the twenty-first century, the age of computers and technology. Many others assume that creation must be opposed to scientific research and inquiry. If God created things supernaturally, then what is there left for scientists to say or do?

The creation worldview is indeed "old," existing since the beginning of time. However, it is by no means outdated. The ideas and implications of creation still make very good sense in our day. Another important point, the creation view is not anti-science. Instead, it opens entire new scientific avenues to explore and research. Creation is good science; it is a refreshing alternative to the barrenness of scientific naturalism. Geology, especially, is a fruitful area for exploring the implications of creation. It involves nothing less than an entire paradigm shift in the interpretation of earth history. The creation week, the great Flood, rapid rates of change — all of these become part of the intriguing creation story.

This is not a comprehensive textbook. General geology material is readily available in other texts. Instead, I have selected particular topics that tend to impact the creation view. Books and journals referenced in the discussion are listed at the end of the book. Scripture verses are taken from the *New King James Version* unless otherwise noted.

There are biblical promises of understanding given to those who diligently seek answers. This may be especially true for those who study the earth from the creation perspective,

speak to the earth,
and it will teach you.
Job 12:8

The goal of this book is to "speak" or interact with the earth and to understand its history.

Chapter One
General Geology

1. What is the creationist view of geology?

Geology is the study of earth's origin, history, and structure. These are *not* dry, dusty topics. Included are volcanoes, earthquakes, seafloor spreading, waterfalls, dinosaur fossils, and beautiful gemstones. There are two broad geology categories, often described as *physical* and *historical* geology. Physical geology deals with rocks and minerals, landscapes, and aspects of the earth's chemistry and physics. Historical geology is concerned with physical changes of the earth over time, and also the fossil record of life from the past. There are many other specialized categories such as geophysics, environmental geology, and structural geology. In recent decades, geology has been expanded to also include surface studies of solar system planets and their moons.

Creationist geology seeks to interpret all earth data in the light of God's Word, the Bible. There is a treasure of information about the earth available in the biblical text. This approach contrasts with *secular* or *naturalistic* geology which is constrained by the assumptions of an immense time scale, very gradual changes, and macroscopic evolution. Unlike physics or chemistry, geology is a science discipline in which *time* is a major factor. Of course, the same physical measurements and data from earth studies are available to everyone. It is the particular assumptions made and presuppositions held which may lead to radically different conclusions. The creationist view presented in this book accepts an earth and universe that were supernaturally created just thousands of years ago. Furthermore, the literal creation week resulted in a fully functioning, mature universe, complete with many kinds of rocks, plants, and animals. The Genesis Flood is further seen as the major factor in explaining the fossil record and also the earth's present-day geography. Because of this emphasis, creationist geology is

1

sometimes described as "Flood geology." Two centuries ago, the dominant view of geology included a young earth and a worldwide Flood. And still today, hundreds of practicing geologists prefer this literal, biblical framework of earth history. Geology is a complex topic and the creationist approach does not easily solve every puzzle and problem. However, there is an exciting, ongoing program of research in geology from the creation perspective.

2. Which early geologists were creationists?

Many pioneer geologists displayed strong Christian testimonies. Unfortunately the biblical foundation of geology, once dominant in universities worldwide, is now nearly forgotten. Some of the individuals presented here may be unfamiliar today, but they were once household names. Not all represent the young-earth position, but each person publicly acknowledged the Creator of the universe. The following representative names are listed alphabetically.

Louis Agassiz (AGG-uh-see, 1807–1873) is called the father of glacial geology. Raised in the Swiss Alps, he recorded telltale evidence for past ice erosion. Agassiz later joined the faculty of Harvard University where he became the foremost naturalist in America. Studies of distinct fossil categories convinced Agassiz that standard evolution theory was false. He was a lifelong supporter of supernatural creation.

Georg Bauer Agricola (1494–1555) spent his life improving the health conditions of miners throughout Europe. By day and night he visited the workers in mines and smelting houses to observe labor conditions. Already in Agricola's day there were spirited environmental debates over mining operations. Agricola based his support for this industry on three biblical points. *First*, the earth was given to mankind to manage and cultivate (Genesis 2:15), including its mineral resources. *Second*, metals could be used in many products to protect life and to improve health as God evidently had planned for mankind. *Third*, all of God's earthly gifts were good, including the natural resources. Agricola also coined the word *fossil* in 1546, which today signifies any permanent record of life from the past. His book *De re metallica* (1530) was a masterpiece of pioneer technical writing in geology. He was the first to classify minerals according to their color, density, and texture. Agricola is known as the father of modern mineralogy.

Louis Bourguet (1678–1742) was a Swiss naturalist with a special interest in mineralogy, like Agricola before him. He was the first to classify the mineral kingdom into clays, stones, metals, and other subdivisions. One of his technical papers in 1729 made the first clear distinction between organic and inorganic (living and nonliving) growth. Bourguet studied stalactites in caves and described their internal radial crystal structure. Bourguet saw crystal organization and other patterns in nature as coming from the direct plan of God. He also believed along with many others that the world's present topography or surface shape largely was due to the effects of the Genesis Flood. Bourguet owned a collection of Bible translations in fifty languages and is said to have read them all. He was truly a student of the earth and also of God's Word.

Parker Cleaveland (1780–1858) authored *An Elementary Treatise on Mineralogy and Geology* in 1816, the first geology text published in the United States. Cleaveland graduated from Harvard College and spent a lifetime exploring the mineral resources of North America. A descendent of Puritan settlers, Cleaveland held to a conservative Christian faith. He avoided the teaching of any geological theory that disagreed with the literal biblical account of creation. This support of creation did not diminish teaching invitations which Parker Cleaveland received from almost every major American college of his day.

William Conybeare (1787–1857) was a British geologist with a special interest in fossils. He wrote the first description of a plesiosaur fossil in *Translations of the Geological Society of London* (1842). This 40-foot marine reptile had a long neck and fearsome teeth. Conybeare stated that the plesiosaur body was designed directly by the Creator for aquatic life. He saw the creature as an exquisite example of the orderliness and diversity of divine creation.

Georges Cuvier (1769–1832) was a masterful teacher, zoologist, and paleontologist. He had the unique ability to correctly predict what a complete animal looked like, based on only one or two bones. Cuvier opposed the theory of gradual evolution. Instead, he believed that fossil formation resulted from catastrophes, especially the Genesis Flood event.

James Dana (1813–1895) was an early president of the Geological Society of America. He traveled widely and became an authority on minerals, volcanoes, and also mountain building. His faculty post was at Yale University. Dana refused to accept the evolution of living things, at least until his declining years. A deeply religious man, he taught the supernatural creation of animal and plant species. Dana's published testimony reads, "By proving the [Bible] record true, science pronounces it divine; for who could have correctly narrated the secrets of eternity but God himself?"

John Fleming (1758–1857) is regarded as Scotland's foremost zoologist and geologist. He had a special interest in physical evidence for the Genesis Flood. Fleming gave detailed descriptions of the initial stages of the Flood with overflowing rivers, bursting lakes, and uprisings of the sea. Fleming also supported Thomas Chalmer's idea of a pre-Adamic world, today called the Gap Theory (Question 90). This approach unnecessarily complicates the Genesis creation narrative, but at least it strongly opposes theistic evolution and evolutionary naturalism.

Richard Kirwan (1733–1812) was a chemist who helped form the Royal Irish Society. This scientific organization continues today, two centuries later. An outstanding mineralogist and creationist, Kirwan objected strongly to fellow geologist James Hutton's vicious attacks on Genesis. Kirwan wrote *Geological Essays* in 1799, promoting a literal view of the Genesis creation account.

Alfred Church Lane (1863–1948) worked as a state geologist both in Michigan and Massachusetts. During his career

Lane published 1,087 technical papers on geology, politics, economics, and religion. He was a lifelong Congregationalist and served as a church deacon for many years. He also volunteered time to the YMCA and Boy Scouts. A plaque in Lane's honor hangs in Goddard Chapel at Tufts College in Medford, Massachusetts. It is inscribed with Lane's own words from many years earlier, "Science and Religion aim to know, to share, and to spread the truth freely."

Johann Lehmann (1719–1767) was an early German geologist. He pioneered stratigraphy, the study of order and sequence in sedimentary rock layers. Lehmann published the first geologic profile diagram in 1756, illustrating underground rock layers. Lehmann firmly believed that fossil-bearing strata had originated during the Genesis Flood. He further taught that the underlying, non-fossil rock, now called pre-Cambrian, was supernaturally formed during the creation week.

John Michell (1724–1793) was a prominent British geologist and astronomer. He is considered the father of seismology for his studies of the disastrous Lisbon, Portugal earthquake of 1755. In 1760 he proposed that earthquake waves could be used to pinpoint exactly where an earthquake originated. His technique for finding an earthquake's epicenter is still used today. In astronomy Michell made the first realistic estimate of the distance to nearby stars. He also determined that many stars orbit others as binary or multiple star systems. During this productive science career Michell also found time for theological training. In his later years, while a member of the British Royal Society, Michell served faithfully as a local church pastor.

Hugh Miller (1802–1859) was a self-taught geologist from Scotland. He wrote several books including an international bestseller about fossil fish titled *Footprints of the Creator* (1849). He argued that the perfection and complexity of fish fossils disproved evolutionary development. Miller successfully combined a career in geology with biblical creation. He warned others that the popular evolutionary ideas of his day would lead eventually to widespread atheism and immorality. A century and a half later his words ring true. He also emphasized the importance of seeing Christ in the Creation. He asserted, "A [mere] belief in the existence of God is of as little ethical value as a belief in the existence of the great sea-serpent." His biographer W.M. Mackenzie wrote in 1905, "Probably no single man since has so powerfully moved the common mind of Scotland."

Bernard Palissy (c. 1509–1590) was a French natural historian who excelled in the varied fields of agriculture, ceramics, and hydrology. Palissy gave the first description of wood petrification by ground water minerals. At the age of 36 he converted to Protestant Christianity. From this point onward Palissy actively integrated his new faith with scientific studies. As one example, in his lectures and agricultural writings, he described the ideal garden as one decorated both with flowers and with biblical quotations. At age 78 Palissy was unfairly imprisoned at the Paris Bastille for his beliefs, where he died.

Grenville Penn (1761–1844) was an amateur geologist, one of the "Scriptural Geologists" of the 1800s. This was a large group of clergymen and geologists in England who opposed the then-popular denial of the global Flood. Penn defended biblical origins in his book titled *A Comparative Estimate of the Mineral and Mosaical Geologies* (1822). His testimony reads: "[Geology] not only conducts the intelligence . . . to the discernment of the God of Nature, but advances it further to a distinct recognition of the God of Nature in the God of Scripture."

Henry Clifton Sorby (1826–1908) was one of the first scientists to apply microscope techniques to geology and metallurgy. He pioneered use of the polarizing microscope to study thin rock sections and to identify minerals. This earned him the title, father of microscopic petrography. Sorby was a loyal, conservative pillar of the Church of England. He belonged to London's Royal Society and was said to have little patience with those members who were anti-religious.

Peter Waage (1833–1900) was a Norwegian mineralogist and chemist. He discovered the chemical law of mass action that determines the proportions of elements that combine into compounds. Waage's Christian faith motivated his life-long evangelistic work with youth. He founded the Young Men's Christian Association (YMCA) in Norway. Waage also campaigned against liquor, having seen its devastating affects within his country.

Johan Gottschalk Wallerius (1709–1785) performed early chemistry and mineralogy experiments in Sweden. His work with soils led him to be called the father of agricultural chemistry. In his day Wallerius was the highest authority on the biblical account of the history of creation. He accepted completely the details of Genesis. At age 67 Wallerius wrote *Thoughts on Creation* (1776) which was translated into many languages worldwide.

George Frederick Wright (1838–1921), born in Ohio, was a founding member of the Geological Society of America. Glacier studies took him to China, Greenland, and throughout North America. Wright promoted the idea of a single ice age that took place about 10,000 years ago. He also believed that people were present during this ice age, an unpopular view in Wright's day. Many creationists would agree with Wright regarding a single, recent ice age. For 38 years Wright edited *Bibliotheca Sacra*, a major theological journal with continuous publication since 1843. This journal is continued today by Dallas Theological Seminary. In later years Wright unfortunately championed the form of Darwinian theology called *theistic evolution*.

3. What Is Catastrophism?

Catastrophism is the concept that many earth features were shaped by major events that occurred rapidly. An early promoter of catastrophism was the French zoologist Georges Cuvier (1769–1832). Cuvier taught that there had been several widespread catastrophes on the earth, the last and most dramatic being the biblical Deluge. Over time most geologists rejected such thinking in favor of very slow, gradual changes on earth. Interestingly, catastrophic events are now once again increasingly used to explain the past. As examples, asteroid collisions are said to be responsible for the formation of the moon, as well as the demise of the dinosaurs. Also the vast "channeled scablands" of eastern Washington State are realized to have eroded very quickly during the Spokane Flood (Question 48). Catastrophism has always played an integral part in creationist geology. The Genesis Flood in particular caused rapid, worldwide changes across the entire earth.

The main alternative to catastrophism is variously called uniformitarianism, naturalism, gradualism, or actualism. This view was expressed two centuries ago by James Hutton and Charles Lyell with the phrase "the present is the key to the past" (Question 5). In Hutton's words, "the past history of our globe must be explained by what can be seen to be happening now." Present-day rates of rock formation and erosion are assumed to have existed over an immense time span, gradually shaping the earth's surface.

Some books wrongly define catastrophism to imply that the laws of nature also must change with time. However, most catastrophists accept the constancy of natural laws, aside from miraculous intervention. It is the constancy of *rates of change* that is in question.

4. What is William Paley's watch argument?

William Paley (1743–1805) was a leading British spokesman for *natural theology*, the study of God's revelation in nature. Paley was a theologian and scholar, trained in mathematics at Cambridge University. He saw complexity and patterns in nature as direct evidence of the Creator's work. In an influential 1802 book, *Natural Theology*, Paley tells an interesting story: Suppose a person walks along a path and notices a stone lying beside the trail. He may wonder where the stone came from but its origin is of little concern. After all, the stone is just one among billions of others. It may be *igneous* in nature, perhaps granite or basalt, formed from cooling magma. Or it may have started out as hardened mud and become *sedimentary rock,* for example shale or limestone. The rock beside the path also may be *metamorphic* or altered rock, such as marble or slate. Whatever its origin, a typical rock is very common and naturally formed.

Now suppose the person walks further along the path and comes upon a *watch* lying beside the path. As before, the question may again arise concerning how this object originated. Let us try the same reasoning used for the earlier rock. The watch may have formed naturally from hot magma, or mud, or from some metamorphic change. But of course these natural explanations are absurd and do not suffice for the watch as they did for the stone. A watch, beautifully constructed and keeping perfect time, *demands* a watchmaker. In the same way the complex designs found throughout the Creation, whether observed in living or nonliving things, also demand a Designer. Consider the human eye, much more complex than a watch. Nature is filled with created patterns, symmetry, and order. The critics of Creation have never adequately answered the design argument from William Paley. It is called the *teleological argument* for the existence of God. An entire study discipline called *Intelligent Design* is based on the order that is continually discovered in nature. Paley's original quote from *Natural Theology* is given in Question 5. Paley was actually echoing the similar thoughts of John Ray, who wrote *The Wisdom of God* a century earlier.

Design remains one of the most powerful and convicting evidences for the supreme Creator. Romans 1:20 further declares that those who ignore this obvious evidence of the Creator are simply without excuse. All things, whether rocks, stars, or insects, demand a Designer. Rocks may look naturally and randomly formed on the exterior. Inside, however, a rock's regular crystal structure is every bit as precise and ordered as the components of a watch. The Creator long ago established the complex chemical rules of atomic bonding which hold the rock firmly together.

5. What are some pertinent geology quotes?

The following quotes are gathered from well-known geologists and other popular spokesmen. The two categories presented are *for* and *against* the creation view of earth history. Those listed in the section promoting creation are not necessarily creationists, and vice versa. However, the quotes on both sides of the issue, whether favoring creation or evolution, are enlightening as to the conclusions drawn by individuals. Names are listed in alphabetical order.

Promoting Creation

All these facts proclaim aloud the one God, whom man may know, adore and love; and Natural History must, in good time, become the analysis of the thoughts of the Creator of the Universe, as manifested in the animal and vegetable kingdoms, as well as in the inorganic world.

Louis Agassiz (1807–1873)
Essay on Classification 1857

Christians desire that their children shall be taught all the sciences, but they do not want them to lose sight of the Rock of Ages while they study the age of rocks; neither do they desire them to become so absorbed in measuring the distance between the stars that they will forget Him who holds the stars in His hand.

William Jennings Bryan (1860–1925)
"Last Message" 1925

If there is any circumstance thoroughly established in geology, it is that the crust of our globe has been subjected to a great and sudden revaluation, the epoch of which cannot be dated much further back than five or six thousand years ago... (in favor of the Genesis Flood).

Georges Cuvier (1769–1832)
Essay on the Theory of the Earth 1817

The whole plan of creation had evident reference to Man as the end and crown of the animal kingdom... The development of the plan of creation... was in accordance with the law of... progress from the simple to the complex.

James Dwight Dana (1813–1895)
Letter 1856

... the number of intermediate varieties, which have formerly existed [must] truly be enormous. Why then is not every geological formation and every stratum full of such intermediate links? Geology assuredly does not reveal any such finely-graduated organic chain; and this, perhaps, is the most obvious and serious objection which can be urged against the theory [of evolution].

Charles Darwin (1809–1882)
Origin of Species 1859

In crossing a heath, suppose I pitched my foot against a *stone*, and were asked how the stone came to be there, I might possibly answer, that, for any thing I knew to the contrary, it had lain there forever... But suppose I found a *watch* upon the ground, and it should be inquired how the watch happened to be in that place. I should hardly think of the answer which I had before given, that for anything I knew, the watch might have always been there. Yet why should not this answer serve for the watch, as well as for the stone?

William Paley (1743–1805)
Natural Theology 1802

It cannot be denied that from a strictly philosophical standpoint geologists are here arguing in a circle. The succession of organisms has been determined by a study of their remains embedded in the rocks, and the relative ages of the rocks are determined by the remains of organisms that they contain.

R.H. Rastall
"Geology"
Encyclopedia Britannica 1954

Geology fully confirms the Scriptural history of the [Flood]... [animals] were buried by the same catastrophe which destroyed them: namely, the Deluge.

Benjamin Silliman (1779–1864)
Yale University
Geological Lectures 1829

In the space of one hundred and seventy-six years the Lower Mississippi has shortened itself two hundred and forty-two miles. That is an average of a trifle over one mile and a third per year. Therefore, any calm person, who is not blind or idiotic, can see that in the Old Oolitic Silurian Period, just a million years ago next November, the Lower Mississippi River was upward of one million three hundred thousand miles long, and stuck out over the Gulf of Mexico like a fishing-rod. And by the same token any person can see that seven hundred and forty-two years from now the Lower Mississippi will be only a mile and three-quarters long, and Cairo and New Orleans will have joined their streets together, and be plodding comfortable along under a single mayor and a mutual board of aldermen. There is something fascinating about science. One gets such wholesale returns of conjecture out of such a trifling investment of fact. (In this humorous description, Mark Twain, challenges unlimited extrapolation, often used in geology.)

Mark Twain (1835–1910)
Life on the Mississippi, 1883

Opposed to Creation

The result, therefore, of this physical inquiry [into the age of the earth] is that we find no vestige of a beginning—no prospect of an end. (This is an expression of gradualism or uniformitarianism, that the present is the key to the past.)

James Hutton (1726–1797)
The Theory of the Earth 1796

Being an attempt to Explain the Former Changes of the Earth's Surface, by Reference to Causes Now in Operation. (This is the lengthy subtitle of a book written to promote uniformitarianism).

Charles Lyell (1797–1875)
Principles of Geology 1830

Nothing in Biology Makes Sense Except in the Light of Evolution (An article title).

Theodosius Dobzhansky (1900–1975)
The American Biology Teacher 1973
Given so much time, the "impossible" becomes possible.
The possible probable, the probable virtually certain.
One only has to wait: time itself performs the miracles.
George Wald
Scientific America 1954

6. What is a Fossil?

A fossil is any permanent remains or trace of plants, animals, or people from the past. This definition includes bones, petrified wood, coal, shells, and footprints. Paleontology is the scientific study of this evidence of earlier life. Categories of fossils and examples include the following:

Actual remains or *body fossils* include bone material, insects trapped in resin, desiccated or dried remains, and frozen flesh. The frozen mammoths of Siberia and Alaska are preserved in this way, as is also the mummification process.

Carbonization or *distillation* is an incomplete fossilization process within rock layers where only a paper-thin residue of carbon remains, precisely outlining the original organism. Delicate leaves and animal forms are sometimes preserved in this way.

Coprolites are fossilized droppings or feces from larger animals. Coprolites provide valuable information on diet and metabolism.

Gastroliths are stomach stones that help animals digest food. These pebbles or small rocks are swallowed by certain animals and kept in their digestive tract. Over time the stones become smooth and polished. Fist-size gastroliths have been found together with dinosaur remains.

Microfossils are tiny one-celled creatures such as diatoms. Combined in great quantities, diatom fossils comprise thick layers of chalk, and also diatomaceous earth (Question 10).

Mineralization occurs when moving groundwater completely dissolves away the flesh and bones of an organism, replacing the hard parts with solid mineral matter. In this way there is a gradual conversion of the buried plant or animal to hard, inorganic material. Closely related, permineralization occurs when minerals are deposited into the pores within an original bone or other dense body parts.

Molds and Casts occur if a buried organism decays away completely, leaving behind a cavity known as a mold. This mold may later be filled naturally with mud, or filled manually with plaster by a fossil hunter. The hardened filling, which then closely duplicates the original animal shape, is called a cast. Natural molds and casts of marine organisms such as clams and brachiopods are quite common. A final category, *trace* fossils include tracks, trails, burrows, nests, and other indications of past animal activity or plant root systems.

7. How is wood petrified?

The word *petrify* means to become stone. It occurs when wood is buried in oxygen-poor sediment so that its decay is inhibited. Water also must move through the ground, carrying dissolved quartz (SiO_2) or calcite ($CaCO_3$) minerals. As this ground water percolates through the wood, it dissolves the original carbon material completely away, cell by cell, and replaces it with the quartz or calcite. Laboratory studies of wood soaked in silica-rich water have shown the start of petrification on a time scale of just days or weeks (Snelling, 1995). Wood posts in mines also have been naturally mineralized in just decades. The actual replacement process is very precise. Petrified wood clearly shows woody tissue, former tree rings, cracks, and bark. The mineralized wood sometimes takes the form of colorful quartz varieties such as agate, chert, and opal. The colors result from impurities in the wood or water. Yellow or red color often results from iron, and green or blue from copper atoms.

There is a rich abundance of petrified wood, especially in places like the Petrified Forest National Park in Arizona. At this location, petrified logs and wood fragments lie in profusion in the desert sands. It appears that many trees were uprooted and transported by raging water. Petrified Forest Monument near Pike's Peak, Colorado, displays a giant tree trunk 17.5 feet (5.3 meters) in diameter. Petrification occurs only rarely today because of the special underground conditions required. However, the plentiful, worldwide occurrence of petrified wood suggests a period in the past with widespread burial of vegetation in water-saturated ground. The Genesis Flood provides an adequate explanation for this abundant type of fossil.

8. Do fossils support evolution?

If one is looking for evidence in support of evolution, the fossil record should be avoided. Instead of revealing numerous connecting links and gradually improving life forms over time, fossils are a strong testimony to the supernatural creation. The following seven conclusions are drawn from the fossils of the earth:

- Fossils reveal that the earth's early, preFlood climate was warmer than today. This ideal, tropical climate may have been due to a surrounding vapor canopy, consistent with some creation models of earth history (Question 40). In contrast, in the evolution view, the sun was dimmer and cooler in the distant past.
- God's creative imagination is infinite. Fossils show that a host of unusual plants and animals lived in the past, including the dinosaurs. The size of many plants and animals was also much larger in the past.
- Creative design is seen in every detail of life. One cannot accurately say that one plant or animal is simpler than another. For example, it is commonly taught that *trilobite* fossils are ancient, primitive ancestors of modern life, having lived 300 million years ago, before the time of the dinosaurs. However, trilobites had complex eyesight that was more "advanced" than the human eye. Trilobite eyes consist of multiple lenses made from the clear mineral calcite, each lens having its own retinal light receptors. Every life

form appears to be uniquely complex and designed from the very beginning of time.

- Most fossils formed rapidly during the worldwide catastrophe of the Genesis Flood. Their formation occurs only rarely today (Wheeler, 1975). Hence fossils are a vivid reminder of the dire consequences of sin. They teach us that the Creator is patient, but judgment day eventually comes.

- Fossils show that plants and animals have remained in distinct categories or *kinds* since the beginning of time. No uncontested connecting link has ever been found in the fossil record. In fact, with the discovery of many new species, there are now far more *missing links* than there were in Charles Darwin's day.

- All efforts to relate one fossil to another on the basis of gradual evolutionary change have been arbitrary and usually temporary. Similarities observed among particular plants or animals show the common plan of the Creator rather than a common ancestry. This is true whether the similarities or "homologies" are on the molecular or anatomical level.

- Fossils of mankind's alleged ancestors always fall into one of two categories. They either are fully human or fully animal-like. No uncontested intermediate form between animals and people has ever been found in the fossil record, nor ever will be.

9. What is an index fossil?

Index fossils are thought to indicate accurately the age of the rock layers in which they are found. Rock formations from different locations containing the same index fossils are assumed to be the same age. Surveyor William Smith first popularized this assumption two centuries ago. To be useful, the fossils should be easily identified, geographically widespread, and limited to a particular span of history. Some index or *guide* fossils and assumed time intervals are shown in Table 1-1 (see also Question 21).

Table 1-1. A list of example index fossils used to date the strata in which they are found. The geologic eras are defined in Table 2-1.

Fossil Type	Millions of Years Ago	Geologic Era
Human remains	0–2	Cenozoic
Dinosaurs	65–120	Mesozoic
Reptiles	100–200	Mesozoic
Belemnites	150–200	Mesozoic (Cretaceous–Jurassic)
Ammonites	150–400	Mesozoic–Paleozoic
Foraminifera	200–350	Mesozoic–Paleozoic
Brachiopods	200–500	Mesozoic–Paleozoic
Sponges	250–550	Paleozoic
Trilobites	at least 300	Paleozoic (Cambrian–Silurian)
Nautilids, Graptolites	400–500	Early Paleozoic

One major problem is that several index fossils later have been found to exist far outside the bounds of their assumed era of time. As examples, coelacanth fish fossils were once associated with the Cretaceous period, gingko tree leaves with the Permian period, and the chambered nautilus with the Silurian period. All three of these examples are now realized to be still living today, and are hence called *living fossils*. Their use as index fossils from the distant past has thus been invalidated. Similar uncertainties remain with all other index fossils which are still in use.

10. What is the most abundant fossil?

This honor belongs to the category of small organisms called diatoms. These are tiny one-celled algae that readily grow anywhere there is light and water available. Algae were once considered plants but are now classified separately because they lack roots, stems, and seeds. Diatoms are found in the soil, in fresh and salt water, in hot mineral springs, and even on polar ice. They comprise the majority of plankton in fresh

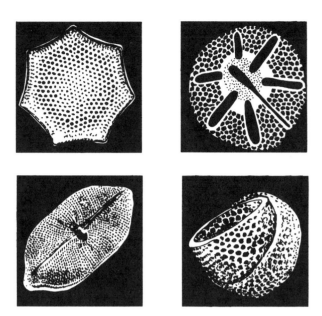

Figure 1-1. Drawings of diatoms, the most common micro-fossil. Each is smaller than a millimeter in size (Kessel and Shih, 1976).

and salt water. These "grasses of the seas" are an essential food supply to all marine life, including the whales. We also rely on oceanic diatoms for our very breath since they continually produce atmospheric oxygen by photosynthesis. Their oxygen output may be greater than that of all the land vegetation combined.

Diatoms encase themselves in tiny silica (SiO_2) or calcite ($CaCO_3$) shells, usually smaller than a millimeter in size. These intricate glass shells are a wonder of design and beauty. They are variously shaped like snowflakes, pinwheels, stars, and complex chandeliers. Figure 1-1 shows several magnified diatoms. They are sometimes called "jewels of the sea." There is unending variety and no diatom shells are found to be exactly alike. Large deposits of these tiny shells comprise "diatomaceous earth" with some accumulations thousands of feet thick. For example the city of Richmond, Virginia rests upon a layer of diatomaceous chalk 50 feet thick in places. Microscopic diatom shells also make up the chalk cliffs of Dover, England, hundreds of feet high. Diatomaceous earth is variously used as a filter, absorber, heat insulator, paint additive, and abrasive. One ounce of ocean floor sediment may contain nearly a million diatom shells. Truly they are an abundant fossil worldwide.

Johann Deidtich Möller (1844–1907) was a German scientist who dedicated his career to the study of microscopic diatoms. He became proficient at mounting these beautiful shells on microscope glass slides, a popular activity a century ago. In 1890 Möller succeeded in arranging 4,026 distinct diatoms in neat rows on a single slide, altogether smaller than a postage stamp (Hoover, 1979). The project took 15 years to complete. No one else has surpassed Möller's artistic talent and patience in displaying these unique symmetric components of the infinitely detailed Creation.

On a larger scale, brachiopod shells are also a very abundant fossil. They occur by the billions worldwide, although living brachiopods are now less common. Also called the *lampshell*, a brachiopod has a clam shell appearance. Thousands of distinct fossil brachiopod species have been catalogued.

11. What is a living fossil?

This is an organism, whether plant or animal, that still survives, although closely similar fossils are found only in "ancient" rock. Charles Darwin first coined the term in his book *Origin of Species* in 1859, referring to the East Asian Ginkgo tree (Eldredge and Stanley, 1984). Fossil ginkgo leaves were found in rocks classified as Paleozoic and dated at 250 million years ago. However, ginkgo trees have been planted in Chinese and Japanese gardens for centuries. They now have been propagated around the world. Ginkgos do well in urban areas where air pollutants weaken other trees. As new living plants and animals are discovered in remote locations, the number of living fossils continues to increase. Another example, crinoids or sea lilies are important Paleozoic index fossils, thought to be between 250–550 million years old. However, there are 700 living species of crinoids, each closely related to the fossils. Living fossils are in conflict with evolutionary change over time. After all, the average lifespan of a species is assumed to be "only" 1–10 million years, with continuous evolutionary change occurring during that time (Vines, 1999), but living fossils show no such change. Table 1-2 shows an entire alphabet of living fossils, together with their alleged time spans on earth. In the case of the marine fish called the coelacanth, the most recent fossils are dated at 65 million years old. Yet coelacanths still swim in the seas, having somehow avoided making fossils for millions of generations.

In the creation view, all of the created kinds of plants and animals lived together from the creation week onward. Therefore there is little surprise at the growing list of discoveries of modern "out-of-place" plants and animals. Each living fossil is a testimony to the creation week.

12. What is the Cambrian explosion?

The Cambrian period is typically dated by geologists at 570–505 million years ago. Within these particular sedimentary rock layers are found the marine fossils of many complex forms of life. They include trilobites, brachiopods, jellyfish, and sponges. These organisms suddenly appear as fossils with no transitional forms or evolutionary ancestors. Paleontologists describe their appearance as an "explosive burst" of evolution. It is concluded that the new animals somehow appeared at breakneck speed, geologically speaking. Paleontologist Stephen Jay Gould once called this unexpected fossil discovery the "enigma of enigmas." One of the best locations for this fossil display is in the Burgess shale formation found in the Canadian Rockies. Charles Wolcott discovered this vast array of unusual, complex marine invertebrates in 1910. His packhorse accidentally turned over a slab of the black shale, revealing exquisite fossils on its surface. Many of these fossils are thin carbon films of strange animals, unlike anything living today. In the creation view, fossil ancestors are not expected for these creatures since they were made during the creation week. Their appearance in the Cambrian rock layers

Table 1-2. An alphabet of living fossils. Their alleged span of time on earth without substantial evolutionary change is given in millions of years.

Ants (100)	Querquedula bird (20)
Bacteria (3500)	Ray (100)
Cockroach (500)	Spider (400)
Duckbill platypus (150)	Shark (400)
Elephant shrew (20)	Starfish (750)
Frog (275)	Scorpion (230)
Gingko tree (200)	Tortoise (275)
Horsetail plant (350)	Tuatara lizard (200)
Isopods, including pill bugs (300)	Uria (10) also called the murre
Jellyfish (600)	bird
Kiwi bird (60)	Vema mollusk (300)
Lungfish (200)	Wollemi pine (65)
Lingula lampshell (450)	Worm (1100)
Magnolia tree (200)	Xiphosorida, horseshoe crab
Nautilus (100)	(200)
Neopilina mollusk (500)	Yucca filamentosa (100)
Opossum (70)	Zalambdalestid mammal (100)
Parrot (70)	

results from preFlood or Flood deposition. Besides the Burgess shale, numerous Cambrian fossils are also found in China, Greenland, Australia, and elsewhere around the world.

13. What is a mass extinction?

These are times in history when geologists believe large numbers of species were quickly eliminated. Five such events generally are recognized, each defining the end of a major geologic time period (Table 1-3). Altogether, 99.9 percent of all species that ever lived are said to be extinct today (Vines, 1999). These extinction events are based on fossil evidence. However, the actual cause of each event is a mystery to science. Suggestions include impacts from space rocks, climatic

Table 1-3. Five mass extinction events as recognized by many geologists. See Table 2-1 for the complete geologic column.

Geologic Period Concluded	Millions of Years Ago	Percent of Species Lost
Cretaceous	66.4	75–80
		Includes the dinosaurs
Triassic	208	55–75
Permian	245	70–90
		"The Great Dying"
Devonian	360	55–75
		Especially marine animals
Ordovician	438	60–85

extremes, sea level changes, volcanism, or wobbles of the earth's rotation axis.

Creationists prefer the idea of just one major extinction that combines all of the apparent separate episodes. This occurred during the Flood, when fossils formed and were separated from each other in rock layers by habitat, mobility, and density variables. These distinct deposits then are misinterpreted as widely separate extinction events.

Some scientists suggest that we are currently living during a new mass extinction event, this time due to habitat destruction by people. The idea is debatable, but it reveals the status of the living world. Rather than seeing the proliferation of newly evolved species, the effort instead is to preserve the plants and animals that remain from the creation week.

14. Do birthstones have mystical properties?

Birthday gemstones were first assigned to particular months centuries ago, perhaps by jewelers who had extra inventory to sell. Gemstone names and colors are shown in Table 1-4. Tradition associates these gems with the twelve astrological signs of the zodiac. In recent years the colorful birthstones have reached a high level of popularity. Of special interest are large crystals of quartz or amethyst. Many customers of these miner-

Table 1-4. A list of birthstones with colors, and alternate gemstones.

Month	Official Gemstone	Color	Alternative Gemstones
January	Garnet	Dark red	
February	Amethyst	Purple	
March	Aquamarine (Beryl)	Pale green	Bloodstone Jasper
April	Diamond	Clear	Sapphire
May	Emerald (Beryl)	Bright green	Agate
June	Pearl	Cream	Moonstone Emerald
July	Ruby (Corundum)	Red	Carnelian Onyx
August	Peridot (Olivine)	Pale green	Sardonyx
September	Sapphire (Corundum)	Deep blue	Chrysolite
October	Opal	Variegated	Tourmaline
November	Topaz	Yellow	Citrine
December	Ruby	Blue-green	Zircon Lapis lazuli

als are not interested in using the gems for jewelry or display. Instead they seek to tap into alleged mystical powers within the crystals. Adherents speak of crystal vibrations that somehow resonate with the planets and also with the mind. This is supposed to result in deeper levels of thought and to bring about an inner harmony with the universe. Such *New Age* terminology is lofty but it is also without support.

Gazing at rock crystals may be preferable to watching television, but any physical or mystical benefit is an illusion. Minerals indeed display fascinating properties including the magnetism of magnetite, the static electricity of amber, and the luster of tiger-eye. The crediting of magical properties to gemstones is actually an ancient idea. Early imagination connected certain minerals with mysterious influences on people. Pearls were thought to represent tears, so they brought sadness to their wearer. Amethyst protected against drunkenness; the name comes from the Greek and means "without alcohol." Bright green emerald was used as a poultice for eye problems. Reddish hematite and also rubies were sought as a treatment for blood diseases. These minerals long ago were worn as amulets, and sometimes were ground up and swallowed. This misuse of earth's inert materials was nonsensical and also dangerous. Most gemstones are simply made of glass or quartz, definitely an unhealthy form of medicine.

Gold and gems were present in the vicinity of the Garden of Eden according to Genesis 2:12, "The gold of that land is good; bdellium (aromatic resin) and the onyx stone are also there." Other gems have formed during earth history by crystal growth underground. Crystals usually gain their beautiful colors from small amounts of impurity atoms. Often just parts per million of a particular atom will give overall color to a crystal.

Twelve precious stones are listed in Exodus 28:15–21. They were a decoration worn upon the breastplate of the Israelite High Priest, representing the twelve tribes of Israel. These stones provided a colorful badge of honor. Aaron was the first to fill the official position of High Priest and to wear these precious stones. Interestingly, twelve jewels will also make up the foundation stones of the New Jerusalem as described in Revelation 21:19–20. These stones surely will add to the majesty and enjoyment of the future celestial city. Contrary to New Age thought, Scripture does not attribute any supernatural power to the earth's rocks and minerals. It is an ancient error to worship mere stones in place of the One who created them. Instead of New Age enlightenment, there has resulted in our day a sad return to a Stone Age of superstition. For all who seek true answers to life, satisfaction is not to be found in minerals from the ground. Instead, peace and unsearchable riches are found only in Christ the Creator.

15. How do new rocks appear in farm fields?

Each spring, many farmers must clear a collection of new rocks from the surface of their freshly plowed fields. It almost seems that the rocks grow and reproduce themselves year by year. This is not the case, of course, but the new rocks appear nonetheless. There are two major contributing reasons. *First*, rocks close to the surface slowly migrate upward in the soil in a process called *frost heaving*. Moisture accumulates beneath rocks while underground. When relatively close to the surface, this water may freeze and expand. Ice crystals draw additional water from the surrounding soil and develop into small ice lenses. As a result, the rock is forced slightly upward. When the ice thaws, soil particles settle to the underside of the rock filling the opening. During many freeze-thaw cycles, the rock is eventually raised upward to the surface of the ground. On a larger scale, frost heaving can damage building foundations, sidewalks, and highways. In very cold regions, bridge pilings and telephone poles gradually have been lifted directly out of the ground by the accumulation of ice beneath them. A *second* reason for new rock appearance in fields is erosion of the soil. Wind may blow the topsoil away, and water runoff may carry it from fields. The heavier rocks then are exposed and left behind. Wind erosion is especially noticeable in a dry environment.

Field rocks themselves have several original sources. Some are part of glacial till, a rocky type of soil deposited by ice age glaciers, often to a considerable thickness (Question 51). Such rock fragments were originally transported from afar by moving ice. Other rocks are eroded and weathered from larger, nearby formations.

16. Do rocks fall from the sky?

In 1807, several large meteorites fell near Weston, Connecticut. They were studied by Yale scientists, but many people remained skeptical of the reports of falling rocks. Thomas Jefferson, in particular, was very suspicious of astronomers who described space rocks. Jefferson reportedly said, "It is easier to believe that Yankee professors would lie than that stones fall from heaven." As sightings and samples accumulated over the years, however, such doubts subsided. There is plentiful debris in the nearby region of space surrounding the earth, including dust, pebbles, and larger rocks. As the earth orbits the sun, the planet's gravity sweeps up some of these particles like a giant vacuum cleaner. Most of the fragments burn up as meteors in the upper atmosphere, causing the familiar *shooting star* appearance at night. These streaks of light are not really stars at all, but instead are small speeding particles which are completely vaporized by friction. You can experience this same type of frictional heating by rubbing your hands briskly together. Larger rock fragments from space may survive the journey through our atmosphere and strike the ground as meteorites. Several times each year the earth passes through particular clouds of debris. Then *meteor showers* or *meteor storms* may occur. At such times a larger number of shooting stars are seen, especially during the hours after midnight. Meteor showers occur annually around January 3, August 12, and December 14. Some years there is a glorious display of celestial fireworks, while other years are a viewing disappointment, depending on the amount of space debris encountered.

Meteorites generally come in three categories. *Irons* are mostly pure iron with about 10 percent nickel content. *Stony* meteorites are made of light-colored silicate material, similar to many earth rocks. The *stony-irons* are a mixture of both types. The origin of these space materials is not certain. Some may come from disintegrated comets, and others from the asteroid belt, a region of large rock fragments located between the orbits of Mars and Jupiter. From a creation perspective, this loose material may date back to the beginning of time as described in Genesis. Alternately the fragments may result from large-scale collisions between solar system objects in the past. In this case, meteorites may be evidence for catastrophism on a large scale.

17. What is the geology of the other planets?

The main geologic difference between the earth and other members of the solar system is our abundance of water. The movement of water and ice continually shape the surface of the earth. Liquid water has been found nowhere else in the solar system thus far. Table 1-5 lists some of the physical extremes of our planet neighbors that are literally out of this world.

The surface of Venus shows rolling hills and is drier than any desert on earth. The mountain peaks of Venus sag under a constant, scorching surface temperature near 900°F (482°C). A lack of craters may hint that the surface of Venus experiences crustal recycling by continental drift similar to the earth. Mars is covered with reddish, rusty sand and rocks. Its valleys and drainage patterns show the unmistakable flow of liquid at some time in the past, whether water or some other fluid. A giant canyon on Mars, called the *Vallis Marineris*, is four times larger than Arizona's Grand Canyon. *Olympus Mons*, an inactive Martian volcano, is fifteen miles (25 km) high and 1200 miles (2000 km) around at its base. This impressive feature is nearly three times the height of Mount Everest.

The large outer planets are gaseous without solid surfaces. Large pressures inside Jupiter, Saturn, Uranus, and Neptune probably result in cores of solid hydrogen. Some astronomers also have suggested that the planetary cores may be rich in carbon compounds. If so, the tremendous internal pressures may squeeze these carbon cores into solid diamond, thousands of miles in size (Ross, 1981). This would make literal "acres of diamonds" on a grand scale, but completely beyond our reach. In recent years, many extrasolar planets have also been detected circling other stars. These new planets display extreme, hostile conditions.

Planetary moons are unique and colorful, as illustrated by Jupiter's four major moons. *Io* is covered with volcanoes and pools of molten sulfur. *Europa* has an icy surface marked by

Table 1-5. A comparison of various properties of the solar system planets. Where appropriate, the values are normalized to a value of one for the earth. Earth values in each case are important for our well being, as chosen by the Creator.

Property	Least	Earth	Greatest
Average distance from sun	Mercury 0.39 au*	1	Pluto 39.5 au
Diameter (Earth 7,920 miles)	Pluto 0.18	1	Jupiter 11.2
Average surface temperature	Pluto −230°C (−382°F)	11.7°C (53°F)	Venus 482°C (900°F)
Air pressure (Earth 14.7lbs/in²)	Mercury, Pluto 0	1 1	Venus 90
Axis tilt	Mercury 2° Jupiter 3°	23.5°	Venus 178° Uranus 97.9°
Rotation period	Jupiter 9.8 hours	24 hours	Venus 243 days
Revolution period	Mercury 88 days	1 year	Pluto 248.5 years
Average orbital speed (miles/hour)	Pluto 10,500	67,000	Mercury 107,000
Mass (Earth 6 x 10²⁴ kg)	Pluto 0.002	1	Jupiter 318
Specific gravity	Saturn 0.71	5.5 5.5	Earth 5.5
Known satellites	Mercury, Venus 0	1	Saturn >30

*au = astronomical units; 1 au = 93 million miles.

dark, narrow fractures. Some scientists think that a deep ocean may underlie the crust. *Ganymede* has a strangely grooved terrain, almost as if a giant comb was dragged across its surface. Here also there is evidence of possible water beneath the rugged surface. *Callisto* is the most heavily cratered object known in the solar system.

Saturn's moon called *Titan* may be covered with lakes of liquid hydrocarbons. Some scientists maintain a futile hope of finding evolved life on Titan. Neptune's moon *Triton* is about the same size as the earth's moon. It displays icy volcanoes that spew out liquid nitrogen at temperatures less than −320°F (−196°C). Clearly the geologic activity of other worlds shows great variety. These many discoveries rule out any simple, evolutionary explanation for the origin of the solar system members. They also show the special care given to the creation of our home planet, the earth.

18. What are some major questions in geology today?

In scientific research, the solution to one problem generally leads to several additional questions, and geology is no exception. Thousands of practicing geologists have gained great insight concerning the earth, but many basic and profound questions remain. Several examples will be listed here.

What really happened to the *dinosaurs*? The currently popular idea calls for an extraterrestrial collision occurring about 65 million years ago. A possible impact site has been identified on the Yucatan Peninsula of Mexico. However, one must wonder why an asteroid collision with the earth would kill off the dinosaurs while many other forms of life remained healthy. Some of the least mobile creatures (tortoises, crocodiles) and also the most sensitive to ecological change (birds, fish) are still with us today. Furthermore, the fossil record does not show an instantaneous demise of all the dinosaurs. Creationists have an alternative view of dinosaur extinction as described in Question 32.

Will it eventually be possible to predict *earthquakes* accurately and precisely to provide an early warning? Much effort has gone into seismic research. This includes the study of pre-earthquake animal behavior, changes in ground water, and gradual ground movement. However, frequent reports of earthquake tragedies show that predictive success is lacking.

What triggers an *ice age*? Geologists have variously proposed volcanic or meteorite dust in the air, a change of the earth's tilt, and even a temporary cooling of the sun. However there is a lack of convincing evidence for any of these ideas. In the creation view, the Ice Age was related to postFlood climate adjustments (Question 51).

The *origin of granite* is not a certainty. As an igneous rock it is assumed to cool from molten material. However, an alternative view is that most granite forms by the reworking of buried sedimentary and metamorphic rocks, aided by liquid solutions that penetrate the rock. This suggested process is called *granitization*. Even though granite is the earth's most abundant rock type, geologists remain unsure of its origin. Nor have they been able to make a synthetic rock in the laboratory equivalent to natural granite (Plummer et al., 1999, p.54).

The Italian Alps include vast exposures of the sedimentary rock *dolostone*. Today, however, the component mineral dolomite $(CaMg(CO_3)_2)$ forms only rarely. There is a mystery of how the worldwide abundance of dolomite originated. There is some evidence that bacteria may have been involved in the process in the past.

Chapter Two
Age of the Earth

19. How old is the earth?

Scientific study is unable to pinpoint the date of the earth's formation. Depending on interpretation, data regarding the earth's age gives a wide range of values, from very short to almost infinitely long. The actual meaning of such data is uncertain because of unknown rates of change and other variables in the past.

The standard view is an earth, moon, and solar system that are 4.6 billion years old. This age is based on radioisotope analysis of meteorites. The universe beyond is assigned an age of 10–15 billion years old. Many creationists believe that these long-age estimates are flawed and that the physical evidence is strong for an earth and entire universe that are only 6–10 thousand years old. Long extrapolation into the past generally is less reliable than the alternative data that supports a recent creation. One wonders why there is such zeal to extend history billions of years into the past, while at the same time there is great hesitation to make science predictions just one hundred years into the future. The assumed requirement for billions of years by the big bang theory and biological evolution is surely a major factor.

In order to determine the time of biblical origin, some have turned to the genealogies of Genesis 5 and 11. The years from Adam to Noah are listed, and also from Noah's son Shem to Abraham. As a fixed point, most scholars believe that Abraham lived around 2,000 BC. Scholars such as Johann Kepler, James Ussher, and John Lightfoot long ago concluded from these biblical passages that the earth and universe were about 6,000 years old. Creation then occurred about 4003 BC, and the great Flood took place around 2350 BC. Other conservative scholars have urged caution in this "adding machine" approach to the Old Testament chronologies. It is uncertain whether the lists of patriarchal names are entirely complete or are meant to be representative. From this viewpoint the calculation of an exact creation date is not possible. Whether one accepts 6 or 10 thousand years of history, both are vastly shorter than the 4.6 billion-year figure commonly assumed for the earth's age. Radioisotope dating, described in Question 26, also has not proven with certainty that the earth is ancient.

James Ussher, in particular, is often ridiculed as being foolish and unscientific for his conclusion that the earth is young. However, he was a brilliant scholar and an expert on Semitic languages including Hebrew, Aramaic, Arabic, and Ethiopic. Along with his Anglican Church duties Ussher was a professor at Trinity College, Dublin, Ireland. Many scholars, past and present who have accepted a recent creation cannot easily be dismissed.

20. What is the difference between relative and absolute age?

Relative dating means that historical events are placed in their proper time sequence without stating the actual ages in years. For example lower layers of sedimentary rock are assumed to be older than upper, overlying rock layers. This assumption is reasonable, except in rare cases where the rock sequence has been overturned.

Absolute dating involves assigning an actual date to a fossil, rock, or other object. For example, the Mesozoic era, the "age of the reptiles," is said to have existed between 245–65 million years ago. Evolutionary assumptions, index fossils, and radioisotope dating are often used to generate such actual numbers. Young earth creationists question the accuracy of many of the published absolute dates for the earth. And they appear to be the only group that challenges the long age assumption of modern science. This serves a valuable purpose in encouraging everyone to carefully check age conclusions.

21. What is the geologic column?

This name is given to the multiple rock layers encompassing much of the earth's crust. During the 1800s these major layers were divided into four eras, then further sub-divided into shorter time periods (Table 2-1). The periods themselves are divided into *epochs*, not shown in the table. The era boundaries are traditionally thought to represent times of major catastrophe and evolutionary change. The rock column does not exist in its entirety anywhere on earth. Missing rock layers at a particular location are assumed to have been removed by erosion. At the Grand Canyon, for example, the Cenozoic and Mesozoic layers are completely missing, except for an erosional remnant at Red Butte. In America's Midwest, it is the Mesozoic era that is absent. Table 2-1 lists the ages that have been assigned to components of the geologic column. The total age span stretches from the present time to 4.6 billion years ago, the earth's assumed age. These numbers are based on assumptions and index fossils, with occasional radio-

Table 2-1. A list of the geologic eras, periods, time spans, and assumed evolutionary examples of living forms at the particular time. The precise boundaries of evolutionary time are not well defined. Dates shown are taken from the Geological Society of America as of 1998.

Era	Period	Millions of Years Ago	Evolutionary Examples
Cenozoic ("Recent life")	Quaternary	1.6 – present	Mankind
	Tertiary	66.4 – 1.6	Mammals
Mesozoic ("Middle life")	Cretaceous	144 – 66.4	Flowering plants
	Jurassic	208 – 144	Birds
	Triassic	245 – 208	Dinosaurs
Paleozoic ("Ancient life")	Permian	286 – 245	Mammal-like reptiles
	Carboniferous	360 – 286	Forests, insects, reptiles
	Devonian	408 – 360	Amphibians
	Silurian	438 – 408	
	Ordovician	505 – 438	First land plants
	Cambrian	570 – 505	First fish
Precambrian		4600 – 570	Bacteria, algae

isotope dating of intruded igneous rock. Note that the Precambrian era is eight times longer than the other eras combined.

The names within the geologic column are derived from various earth locations. The *Cambrian* period comes from the Medieval Latin word for Wales. These particular rock strata were first studied in Wales, and show evidence for original warm seas and desert land areas. *Devonian*, the "age of fishes," is named for Devonshire, England, where fish fossils are found in great abundance. The *Carboniferous* period, meaning "carbon bearing," referred originally to English midlands where beds of coal commonly occur. In the former province of Perm, Russia are found flat-lying beds of red rock in the *Permian* period. The *Jurassic* period is named after the Jura Mountains separating France and Switzerland. The *Cretaceous* period refers to the "age of chalk," named for the chalk cliffs of Dover, England.

Current research by creationists concerns the question of which portion of the geologic column accumulated during the Genesis Flood. One popular view is that the lowermost Precambrian rock is original, created crust. Then all the overlying layers may be Flood deposits, up through the Cenozoic era. Creationists thus challenge the basic assumption that rock strata form very gradually over time. Depositions of sand grains have been studied in flumes which are large tanks of moving water (Berthault, 1994). It is found that a swift current causes distinct layers to form quickly (Figure 2-1). Similar results are also reported in the mixing of dry powders (Weiss, 2003). If this process was dominant during the Genesis Flood, then the geologic column is greatly misinterpreted by many geologists.

22. What has Surtsey Island taught us?

One November morning in 1963, a fisherman stood on the deck of his boat just off the southern coast of Iceland. He noticed a strange sulfur smell, somewhat like rotten eggs, and then smoke and hot rocks began rising from the sea. By eve-

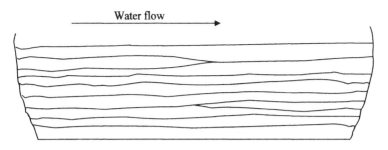

Figure 2-1. A sketch of distinct sediment layers formed under water by a swift current. Each layer is millimeters or centimeters thick.

ning, volcanic debris had begun to form the new Island Surtsey, named for a mythological Icelandic god of fire.

Volcanism on Surtsey continued for about two years and formed a mile-size island. Soon the wind and waves carved out ancient-looking beaches of black sand. Even before the island cooled, seabirds visited, bringing with them seeds and insects. Spiders also glided to Surtsey on silken threads. Lichens and mass grew on the lava rock and began converting it to soil. Seals now bear their young on Surtsey's beaches. This northern island, just decades old, already has the appearance of mature age. Surtsey taught us that the created earth is programmed to quickly heal its scars and to provide habitats for living creatures. The new island cautions us that many earth features may not be as old as they appear.

23. If the earth is young, why does it look so old?

Physical appearance is of limited value in determining age. Whether one considers the age of a person or a feature of the earth, looks can be very misleading. Many regions of the earth show evidence of dramatic, sudden change instead of inactive eons of time. Even the Grand Canyon, often called a "monument to time," displays startling youthfulness in the Genesis Flood interpretation. An important factor in measuring time periods is the related *rate of change*. If changes upon the earth must occur very slowly, then there is indeed a long span of history. If past changes have happened quickly, however, whether by flood, erosion, or some other catastrophe, then the earth's age may be quite young. Hundreds of geologists today, whether secular or creationist in worldview, believe that rapid, catastrophic changes have shaped the earth. In this interpretation the earth actually does not look old. A sound scientific argument can be made that the earth is less than 10,000 years old, not billions of years.

Consider just one typical geologic feature that is often used to promote an ancient earth. *Varves* are thin layers of sediment, alternating light and dark in color, and hardened into rock. These layers sometimes number in the thousands. Each individual layer is traditionally interpreted as an annual deposition of mud in a lake. However, it is now realized that the multiple sediment layers may form rapidly due to storms that stir the lake bottom. Varves are not necessarily annual layers covering a long period of time.

Sedimentary strata and imbedded fossils are found in many places worldwide. A slow formation of these rock layers is usually assumed. However, *polystrate fossils* tell a different story. These are fossils that extend or cut through more than one rock layer, for example petrified tree trunks. How could an upper tree trunk stand in the open for millions of years, waiting to be gradually buried in silt? The tree would surely decay and disappear. One of the most interesting polystrate fossils on record is a baleen whale. In 1976 it was found lying in a tilted (40°–50°) bed of diatomaceous earth in a quarry at Lompoc, California (Russel, 1976; Corliss, 1980). This amazing fossil is 80 feet long, and was evidently buried quickly in a Flood catastrophe.

24. What are radiohalos?

These halos are small defects found within igneous rock, usually in granite. They result from the decay of tiny concentrations of radioactive atoms within the rock sample. Typically, a small quantity of the radioactive mineral zircon is embedded within grains of biotite, a component of granite. The decay radiation causes crystalline defects around these radioactive "pockets." The defects appear as regions of dark discoloration, actually spherical in shape. The spheres are only a few millionths of a meter in diameter (microns) and require a microscope for examination. They have been studied extensively by researcher Robert Gentry (1986). Halos are also reported in coalified wood.

Of particular interest to creationists is the halo formed by the decay of polonium 218, one of the heavier radioactive isotopes. Each element has several forms, or isotopes, with different weights. Polonium 218 half-life is just 3.05 minutes. This means that a concentration of radioactive polonium 218 will be completely disintegrated within about 30 minutes, after 10 half-lives. The halos formed by this decaying polonium are found to be abundant in granite rocks. There is one important condition necessary for halo formation: They occur only in solid, crystallized rock. If radioactive decay occurs within molten rock material, called magma, no crystal defect halo can form. It therefore appears that the many observed halos must have formed within granite which had cooled and hardened almost instantly, during the short polonium 218 lifetime. However, granite is usually assumed to have cooled from a melt over a very long time scale. An alternative view is that the rock may have been supernaturally created in a cooled, crystalline form, complete with pockets of radioactive Po-218 in place. Whatever the case, the existence of the polonium halos is evidence *against* the assumed slow cooling of granite.

Another possible answer to the polonium mystery is that fresh radioactive atoms may be supplied to hardened granite rock, perhaps carried by moving groundwater under high pressure. Polonium 214 is known to be a decay product of uranium 238. If new polonium is continually supplied in this way, then the other decay stages of uranium 238 should also make identifiable halos in the rock. However, they are often not present with the polonium halos. Thus it appears that polonium was *itself* inserted in the original, hardened rock.

Many radiohalos are found in rocks that creationists interpret as originating during the Flood. This further supports the idea of rapid water transport of radioisotope material into newly-forming rocks (Snelling, 2000, p. 390). As in all scientific analysis, further data and other possible interpretations are being studied. Halos may or may not continue to be a strong creationist argument. Meanwhile, the burden is upon secular geologists to explain the appearance of polonium radiohalos.

25. How quickly do batholiths cool?

The word *batholith* means "deep rock." It refers to large masses of rock, often many square miles in area, assumed to have formed underground as magma slowly cooled and hardened. Most batholiths consist predominantly of granite. Examples include the roots of many mountain ranges.

It is usually assumed that batholiths cooled very slowly over millions of years. Afterall, the magma is well insulated in the deep underground. However, one should not underestimate the work of moving ground water in carrying away heat. Rapid water circulation could greatly reduce the cooling and formation times for batholiths. Since batholiths form beneath the surface, their solidification has never been observed. Therefore their actual formation time remains an open question. Batholiths are not necessarily ancient in age (Question 24).

26. How does radioisotope dating work?

Certain kinds of atoms are unstable or radioactive. This is usually because of an excess number of neutrons in their atomic nucleus. After a period of time the atom disintegrates, emitting radiation in the process. The original "parent" atom changes into an entirely different "daughter" atom. As examples, carbon-14 turns into nitrogen, and uranium eventually turns into lead. Now suppose an object is originally formed with a certain number of parent atoms within it. As this object ages, the number of parent atoms decreases and the number of daughter atoms increases. If the *half-life* of the parent atom is known, an age for the object can then be determined from the composition of its atoms. Half-life measures the average lifetime of radioactive atoms. During one half-life, 50 percent of a collection of the atoms will decay. Table 2-2 gives some examples of decaying atoms and their half-lives. Except for carbon-14, the listed isotope examples are commonly used for rock dating.

The radioisotope dating method involves chemical analysis to determine the ratios of parent and daughter atoms in the sample (Figure 2-2). These include the ratios of uranium to lead, rubidium to strontium, and potassium to argon. This analysis is very precise, measuring parts per billion or parts per trillion of atoms. Age results in the range of millions or billions of years are not unusual. However, these calculated ages are subject to interpretation. Numbers of atoms can be accurately measured, but what does this data really mean? Assumptions must

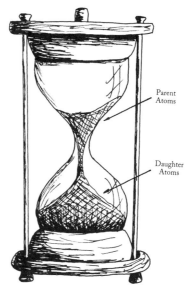

Parent Atoms

Daughter Atoms

Figure 2-2. An illustration of radioisotope decay. A rock sample is pictured by the hourglass. The radioactive parent atoms and their daughter produces are represented by sand grains.

be made about the initial composition of the sample along with any changes that may have occurred during the history of the sample. For example, parent or daughter atoms may have migrated into or out of the sample, invalidating the calculated age. Also many creation scientists believe that radioactive decay was greatly accelerated at some point in history, perhaps at Creation, or at the time of the curse of Genesis 3, or else during the year of the Genesis Flood. This would result in a rapid accumulation of daughter isotopes, and apparent great age.

Table 2-2. Some representative radioisotope parents, daughter products, and half-lives. Also shown are some commonly dated materials.

Parent Isotope	Daughter Isotope	Half life (years)	Materials Commonly Dated
Carbon-14	Nitrogen-14	5,730	Plant, animal remains, shells, glacial ice
Potassium-40	Argon-40	1.25 billion	Biotite, volcanic rocks
Rubidium-87	Strontium-87	48.8 billion	Muscovite, igneous and metamorphic rocks
Samarium-147	Neodymium-143	106 billion	Metamorphic rocks, meteorites
Rhenium-187	Osmium-187	43 billion	Ore deposits, meteorites
Thorium-232	Lead-208	14.1 billion	Zircon
Uranium-235	Lead-207	704 million	Zircon, pitchblende
Uranium-238	Lead-206	4.5 billion	Zircon, pitchblende

Carbon-14 dating is in a separate category from the other radioisotope techniques. This method applies mainly to vegetation that absorbs carbon-14 during its lifetime. When the plant or tree dies, its carbon intake then ceases and its acquired C-14 slowly converts back to nitrogen. The amount of remaining radioactive carbon-14 is measured for samples. The C-14 technique is used extensively in archaeology with many useful results. For example the Shroud of Turin has been tentatively shown by C-14 to date from medieval times instead of the New Testament era. If true, the shroud cannot be the Lord's burial cloth as some insist. It has been suggested that the C-14 test dated only an outer coating of the Shroud, or contamination from a fire in 1534, not the cloth itself. Further research may be needed to verify the antiquity of the Shroud. In contrast, radiocarbon dating found the Dead Sea Scrolls to be truly ancient, dating back to 200 BC. The similarity of these scrolls to our present Scripture shows that the

Lord has preserved the accuracy of his word throughout history. Beyond carbon-14, the other radiometric methods, involving long-lived atoms and applied to rock samples, are much less reliable.

Radioisotope dating should be placed in a similar category to other scientific dating techniques. All of them are fallible and none should be solely relied upon, whether they give an ancient age or a recent age for the earth. Unfortunately the interpretation of radiometric dating results is intertwined with the evolutionary assumption of an old universe and earth. The reinterpretation of such results is an active area of creation research.

27. What is dendrochronology?

Dendrochronology is the scientific study of climate history using tree rings. Most trees produce rings during their annual growing season. The *cambium* layer lies just inside a tree's bark. Each year the cambuim grows outward to form a new layer. The resulting rings can be observed in living trees by using an *increment borer* tool. A drill enters the tree trunk to its center and a pencil-thin wood core is withdrawn. This core is then split apart and the ring widths measured. The internal makeup of each ring is a "fingerprint" for the climate conditions during its year of growth. Living bristlecone pine trees have as many as 4,770 rings (*Discovery*, 2002). Bristlecones grow in several western states and are the oldest living things on earth. Their record of growth rings reveal historical climate changes, solar cycles, forest fires, air pollutants, and insect invasions.

Dendrochronology was first pioneered by astronomer Andrew E. Douglas in 1901. Over the years, charts have been compiled that correlate tree rings with actual dates. Figure 2-3 illustrates how several trees with overlapping dates can be compared. Dates have been assigned to wood samples including German oaks, Lebanese cedars, shipwreck timbers, and roof beams. Bristlecone pines have the longest time series, claimed by experts to stretch back to approximately 7040 BC

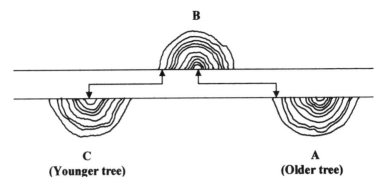

Figure 2-3. An illustration of dendrochronology. The curved lines represent tree rings. Tree A may be a buried log, tree B an old fence post, and tree C a living specimen. In this simplified drawing, an outer ring of an earlier tree is correlated with an inner ring of a more recent tree.

(Gidwitz, 2001). It is interesting that longer spans of time do not appear possible using trees. Dendrochronology is an absolute dating method that does not necessarily conflict with the recent creation view (Bates, 2002).

28. Is ocean salt an age indicator?

The seas contain an immense amount of dissolved sea salts. The term "salt" refers chemically to any molecule containing both metal and non-metal atoms. Salts include common table salt or sodium chloride ($NaCl$), and also magnesium chloride ($MgCl_2$), sodium sulfate (Na_2SO_4), and potassium bromide (KBr). Sodium chloride comprises 68 percent of sea salt.

Salts continually are washed into the sea by the world's rivers, derived from weathered rocks. Much dissolved salt also arrives by way of hydrothermal vents on the ocean floor. Thousands of these "black smokers" spew out mineral-rich water. Small amounts of salt leave the ocean by sea spray and by evaporation. Ocean salt may also be incorporated into clay minerals, and in some cases it may crystallize. Taking these processes into account, it is thought that today's oceans are slowly increasing in salinity. The oceans currently contain

3.5–3.7 percent salt by weight. In contrast, the Dead Sea contains 25 percent salt and is saturated (Question 88). By estimating the current salt input and output along with total salt content, one can calculate an age for the oceans. This method was first suggested by astronomer Edmund Halley (1656–1742). The calculation was carried out a century ago by Irish scientist John Joly (1857–1933), and more recently by Austin and Humphreys (1991). To repeat the calculation, consider some modern estimates for the total amounts of the element sodium:

Total ocean content	14,700 trillion tons
Rate of influx	400 million tons/year
Rate of loss	200 million tons/year

A maximum age for the oceans is found by dividing the total content by the rate of accumulation,

$$\frac{14,700 \, \text{trillion tons}}{200 \, \text{million tons/year}} = 73 \, \text{million years.}$$

If the created ocean began with some initial salt content, as is likely, then this maximum age is too large. The ocean age also is less if salt influx was greater in the past.

The present salinity of the oceans is a strong evidence for their youthfulness. How then is it possible that life began in early, primordial oceans several billion years ago, as commonly assumed? Creationists await a convincing explanation for this large discrepancy in time.

29. Are coral reefs an age indicator?

Coral consists mainly of calcium carbonate, or limestone. The mineral is extracted from seawater by tiny marine organisms called polyps to build their living structures. The hard framework of tiny hollow tubes then remains as a permanent rock formation. Coral colonies may accumulate as reefs, atolls, or entire islands in warm shallow seas. The Enewetok Atoll in the western Pacific Ocean has a coral thickness of about 1400 meters. At present rates of growth, some large reefs are estimated to be hundreds of thousands of years old. However, present growth may be slow compared with the past. Coral formation depends strongly on water temperature, concentration of dissolved minerals, and the number of reef-building organisms. Reefs grow best when water temperature is above 18°C (64°F) and depth is less than 40 meters. On occasion, very rapid coral growth has been observed. A new reef formed after the 1883 Krakatoa (also Krakatau) volcano, growing at several inches of thickness per year. Therefore the present size of coral reefs may not be an accurate indicator of age. In addition, there is some question of whether formations such as Enewetok Atoll *are* actually coral reefs which grew in place (Oard, 1999).

Coral exists in abundance worldwide. The Great Barrier Reef along Australia's Northeast coast is 1260 miles (2100 km) long and 10–90 miles (17–150 km) wide, covering an area of 80,000 square miles. Even in inland areas like America's Midwest there are many carbonate formations containing corals and other marine fossils. These may have formed when shallow marine water covered the Great Lakes region, either in preFlood or postFlood times. It also should be added that many structures once interpreted as fossil coral reefs are now recognized as large debris blocks, transported by turbulent flood water.

30. Does stalactite growth require millions of years?

Stalactites are mineral "icicles" which form on the roof of a cave from dripping water. As the water evaporates, calcite, quartz, or other minerals are left behind to build up formations. Stalagmites may also grow upward from the floor of a cave, and some caves have large columns resulting from the eventual joining together of stalactites and stalagmites. *Dripstones* and *speleotherms* are general names for cave formations.

The common assumption is that these cave features require eons of time for their formation. However, the timescale depends strongly on the amount of water available and also its mineral and carbon dioxide content. Other variables include cave temperature, humidity, air currents and water temperature. Actually, little is known about the rate of growth of stalactites. Even if the rate of mineral growth within a cave is slow today, conditions may have been far different in the past. In the years directly following the great Flood, especially, there may have been a much larger amount of underground, circulating mineral water.

There are many known examples of rapidly formed stalactites. They sometimes grow under concrete bridges, or in tunnels, cellars, and mines. Such stalactites obviously formed in a span of only decades, not millions of years. When derived from concrete, mineral formations usually consist of calcium hydroxide, $Ca(OH)_2$, instead of calcite, $CaCO_3$. The hydroxide material is typically soft and flaky. Creation research demonstrates the rapid formation of the hard $CaCO_3$ form of stalactites under ideal conditions (Williams, et al., 1981).

31. Is earth's magnetism an age indication?

All magnetism, whether that of a horseshoe magnet or an entire planet, arises from circulating electrical currents. When electrical charge moves in a circle, a magnetic field is established inside and perpendicular to the loop. Perhaps you have magnetized a nail or screwdriver by wrapping an insulated wire around it, then connecting a battery. After removing the battery and wire, the tiny electron orbits of atoms may remain permanently aligned within the magnetized metal object.

The actual source of the earth's magnetism is something of a mystery. Albert Einstein once described geomagnetism as one of the chief unsolved problems of physics, and it remains so today. The earth's field cannot result from permanently magnetized material beneath the ground. Heat destroys the magnetism of metals, and internal earth temperatures reach thousands of degrees. Instead there must be internal circulating electrical currents, probably within the earth's liquid outer core, about 2000 miles (3218 km) deep. The total strength of the earth's magnetism requires this underground electric current to total billions of amperes.

Measurements during the past two centuries show a gradual decrease of the earth's magnetic field. Probably frictional resistance is affecting the internal electrical current. Estimates give a possible decay of earth's magnetism to near zero strength in just thousands of years (Humphreys, 2002). This has important implications for mankind since the earth's magnetic field protects us from harmful solar radiation. Without the protective magnetic shield, all life on earth would be endangered.

Many geologists speculate that there is a *dynamo* mechanism that causes the earth's magnetism to regenerate itself following decreases and occasional reversals of its north and south magnetic poles. There may indeed have been temporary magnetic reversals in the past, perhaps connected with turbulence within the earth during the Genesis Flood event. A straightforward view of earth's magnetism sees it as an indicator of a young earth. The field was established at creation, some thousands of years ago. Over time this field then is gradually diminishing in strength.

32. What is the creationist view of dinosaurs?

These impressive creatures were part of the original creation week. On the fifth day, flying creatures and sea life appeared. This included the flying reptiles such as pterodactyls and also the marine reptiles such as the plesiosaurs. Land dinosaurs then were made along with cattle on the following sixth day of creation (Gen. 1:20–25). Evolution theory teaches that dinosaurs died out 65 million years ago in a "land before time," long before man appeared on the earth. However, creation presents the contrary view that man and dinosaurs actually lived together on the early earth just a few thousand years ago. Multiple evidences for this coexistence include the following points:

Traditional stories and legends about dragons exist in many cultures. These creatures are often very similar to dinosaurs in description. The stories may have developed from actual dinosaur encounters with people in the distant past.

There are possible footprints of humans and dinosaurs in the same rock strata, found at many different locations worldwide. These include the western states and also in Russia. In these cases, dinosaurs and humans appear to be in the same location at the same time.

Sketches of dinosaurs and dragons exist on ancient cave walls in many locations worldwide. These early artists likely drew what they observed in nature.

Detailed descriptions of dinosaur-type creatures are given in Job 40–41. They are called *behemoth* and *leviathan*, and are described as land and sea animals similar to dinosaurs and marine reptiles. The behemoth may have been an apatosaur (brontosaur), living in the Jordan River Valley in the postFlood years. Job evidently was familiar with these animals, and he lived around 2,000 BC, following the Flood.

Still-living creatures somewhat similar to dinosaurs are the Komodo Dragons of Indonesia. These 10-foot monitor lizards weigh 300 pounds, and have a poisonous bite and large claws. They are not dinosaurs, but resemble them in some ways. Another example is the Tuatara lizards of New Zealand. These creatures are called "living fossils," already having been present in their modern form when dinosaurs were alive.

In 1977 Japanese fishermen discovered a deceased plesiosaur-like creature in the South Pacific Ocean. Its body was 33 feet long and it weighed almost 4,000 pounds. The identity of this sea monster remains uncertain. There are many similar reports of unusual carcasses washed up on seashores worldwide, over the centuries.

Scripture is very helpful in unlocking secrets about dinosaurs. For example, secular science cannot determine with certainty the diet of these animals. However, Genesis 1:30 explains that all creatures, as well as mankind, were initially plant eaters, or herbivores. Then, following the Flood, mankind and presumably the animal world were given the option of eating meat (Gen.9:3). Many modern science conclusions about dinosaurs agree with Scripture, including the following:

Apparent dinosaur nests have been located in Montana and in China, showing that parents provided for their young with food and protection. Parental love and care have always been God's way of filling the earth, both for mankind and for the animal kingdom.

Some dinosaurs may have been warm-blooded. They traveled in large herds and nested in colonies or nurseries. They were magnificent creatures with designed bodies and a complex social behavior. In other words, they were not a primitive, low-level branch on the evolutionary tree as commonly portrayed. Instead they were a part of God's marvelous, perfect creation.

Dinosaurs, like modern reptiles, continued to grow larger as long as they lived. Crocodiles have this characteristic today, some reaching lengths of more than 30 feet (9.1 m). Long lifetimes on the early earth with its ideal climate led to the great size of many dinosaurs, the largest land creatures of all time.

Unexpected surprises often arise in dinosaur studies. For example, footprints of an unknown dinosaur in France show that it may have hopped about like a kangaroo (DeYoung, 2000). It is now thought that some dinosaurs were fast moving creatures, capable of bursts of speed. The protruding blades on the back of Stegosaurs have been found to be cooling "radiators" which helped prevent overheating. The Supersaurus, a 40-foot tall, 30 ton dinosaur, had hollow hipbones. The interior of the large bone has a lattice of smaller bones arranged somewhat like corrugated cardboard (Figure 2-4). There are also multiple openings in dinosaur skulls. This design decreased the animal's weight while maintaining great strength. Such unending variety and purpose in the makeup of living things is expected of the Creator, the Master Designer.

What finally happened to the dinosaurs? Scientists have generated a long list of possibilities. They suggest that the earth became too warm, too cool, too dry, or too wet. Alternatively a colliding comet, meteorite, or perhaps a volcanic eruption is said to have raised vast quantities of dust into the air. This dust layer stopped the growth of vegetation that dino-

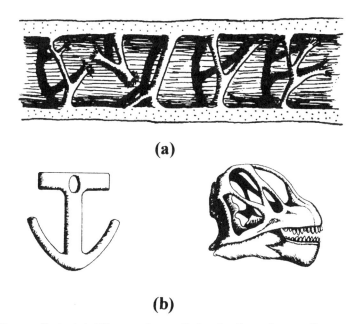

(a)

(b)

Figure 2-4. (a) Illustration of the hollow bone design of some large dinosaurs and pterosaurs. The figure includes bone deterioration that occurred after death. (b) The camarasaur backbone vertebra and skull with designed openings to reduce weight (DeYoung, 2000).

saurs needed for food. An alternate idea from the biblical perspective involves the ice age that followed the Genesis Flood (Question 51). Most dinosaurs perished in the Flood along with other animals. Following this event, dinosaurs from the ark began to reproduce. However, the cooler postFlood climate may have hindered their repopulation efforts after they left the ark. In certain locations, perhaps some of the dinosaur kinds were able to survive for centuries following the Flood, thus leading to the Job 40–41 eyewitness descriptions of these impressive creatures.

33. What do we learn from ice cores?

Ice cores are deep samples of polar ice accumulations from the past. The cylindrical cores are typically 4–5 inches (10–13 cm) in diameter and are obtained using a hollow drill. These ice cores contain valuable information about past climates. They reveal seasonal snowfalls along with wind patterns and air pollutants. In this way, much valuable historical information remains "frozen in time." The core samples may reach ice depths to thousands of feet.

Fine layers seen within the ice cores are often interpreted as annual records dating back hundreds of thousands of years. However it is also possible to fit ice core data into a recent-creation time frame. In this view there has been one major ice age which directly followed the Genesis Flood (Question 51). Many of the ice layers were accumulated during this time, representing frequent storms rather than long age, annual events. Ice then has continued to accumulate up to the present day. Altogether there are several thousand years of ice accumulation, but not necessarily tens or hundreds of thousands of years of history.

One aspect of ice core data from Greenland is especially interesting. During the 1990s, an ice core from a 2-mile depth was withdrawn. It shows a very rapid warming of the earth at the end of the ice age (Hoffman and Schrag, 2000). In secular science there is no agreement on what triggers an ice age in the first place, and its rapid termination is even more of a mystery. In contrast, the creation view has a general mechanism in place. For several centuries following the Flood, the oceans were relatively warm. This resulted from volcanism during the worldwide Flood, much of it occurring beneath the ocean surface. The warm seas in turn led to increased evaporation and precipitation. In the polar regions, snow and ice therefore accumulated in great amounts. This ice eventually comprised the continental ice sheets. The earth later warmed again with the growth of vegetation worldwide, along with many other physical and chemical adjustments of the earth, bringing the ice age to a close.

34. Where do cavemen fit into biblical history?

There have always been cave dwellers on earth, including the present day. Caves provide natural protection and climate control that long have been utilized worldwide by displaced or nomadic people, hunters, and settlers. There are dozens of cave references in Scripture, whether used as homes, hiding places, or tombs. See Job 25: 9–11 for a description of mining for riches in a cave or shaft. One should not be misled by the false impression that early cave dwellers were primitive, ape-like creatures that were inferior to us. The early art and tools often found in caves show that early inhabitants were intelligent and culturally refined.

There are certain hazards to living in a cave. The humidity, darkness, and cool temperatures can aggravate health problems such as arthritis. This may be the reason why the remains of some early cave dwellers show them possibly to have been stooped over with bone disease. However, these fossil remains do not necessarily date back to ancient "prehistoric" times. In the creation view, bones and artifacts from cave areas date from relatively recent postFlood times as people explored the new, unfamiliar landscape. This view places existing cave-man evidence within the last four or five thousand years.

35. Was there a stone age or an iron age?

Cultures, both past and present, always make use of readily available materials for their implements and tools. If stone or iron is the plentiful resource of a region, this may naturally lead to a stone or iron-using culture. However it is wrong to picture such people as an early evolutionary link to modern man. In truth, all of these historical groups were fully human. As evidence, our ancestors designed and used tools that require abstract thinking. The term "stone age" with its ancient, primitive connotation is misleading since there are still such groups living today in remote areas of the earth. The term *paleolithic* refers to the use of simple stone implements. *Neolithic* refers to the more involved use of shaped or polished stone tools and weapons.

As one modern example, consider the Native American Indian named *Ishi*. A last survivor of the Yahi tribe, Ishi lived in California wilderness until 1911. That year, hunger drove him to cross over and enter the modern world. He was housed at a San Francisco museum until his death six years later. Ishi is often classified as a stone age Indian. However, he demonstrated many advanced talents at living in harmony with nature. These included archery, herbal medicine, and food preparation. Ishi was by no means primitive. His story is told in Theodora Kroeber's 1961 book, *Ishi in Two Worlds*.

When did some of the past "stone age" cultures thrive? In the years following the great Flood, new generations had to adjust to a severe, colder climate. Many people during this early postFlood era were forced to live in caves or the outdoors. Some were hunters who used available resources, whether stone, flint, or metal. Another major period of cave culture probably followed the Tower of Babel episode described in Genesis 11. The confusion of languages caused people to spread outward in all directions from the Mesopotamian region. Some of these splinter groups quickly lost the technical edge that had developed in Babylon, and were forced to "start over from scratch." This may account for much of the evidence of stone age dwellers that is found today on nearly every continent. The picture is somewhat similar to American pioneers who left mature cities in Europe to live in log cabins and sod houses on the new frontier of North America.

Biblical archaeologists divide Palestine history into several categories including Early Bronze I (3100–2900 BC), II (2900–2100 BC), III (2600–2300 BC), and IV (2300–2100 BC). The Middle Bronze age, around 2000 BC, was the time of Abraham. During these time spans one finds a progression toward greater population, increased trade, intricate pottery, and writing. These time periods provide a useful and valid classification system for archaeologists. Stone and iron ages do not support human evolution, but instead are a record of the biblical history of mankind.

36. How many total people have lived on the earth?

In the creation view mankind began with our first parents, the literal Adam and Eve. The human family rapidly grew in size until the time of the Genesis Flood, possibly reaching several million people. Only eight souls survived the Flood on board the ark. The postFlood world population then recovered to its present value of over six billion people. When unrestrained, population typically increases in an exponential or geometric form. This means that in a certain span of time the population doubles. The current doubling time for world population is about 53 years at 1.3 percent annual growth.

The long-age view of earth conflicts sharply with current population trends. A geometric population growth over hundreds of thousands of years leads to grossly excessive numbers for the present population. Therefore, it is usually concluded that the great majority of human history saw a static, unchanging population. An estimated 50 billion people have lived throughout human history (Westing, 1981). Two-thirds of this total is thought to have lived since AD 1200. Today's population is 12 percent of the assumed total.

Many creationists limit earth history to about 10,000 years. Thus there is no need to assume an unproven, long period of static, non-changing population. Instead, a realistic, conservative population growth rate over just ten millennia or less leads directly to today's world population. The detailed analysis is complicated by numerical uncertainties of the preFlood population, wars, plagues, and natural disasters. The total number of people over all time, in the creation view, could well be close to that of secular estimates, 50 billion souls.

A related question concerns how many different species have lived on the earth. By one definition, a species is a category of animals or plants within a genus, capable of interbreeding among its members and producing fertile offspring. For example, horses and donkeys are separate species. They can breed and produce a mule, but the mule is sterile and cannot reproduce further. The word *species* as used today is probably a much narrower division of living things than the created biblical "kinds" described in Genesis 1:24.

The total number of plant and animal species in our world is not known. The current estimate is between 40 and 80 million species, the majority living in tropical rain forests (Salter and Hobbs, 2003). Whatever the total number of species, it is probably decreasing due to disease and habitat loss. There is great emphasis today on protecting certain species that are endangered. This is a worthy goal of caring for the Creation as long as it is conducted within reason. There is a biblical command in Genesis 1:26 for us to rule over, or manage, the plant and animal world. It should be noted that species loss is an opposite trend to the evolutionary prediction of ever-increasing numbers of species. Instead, we are trying to "hang on" to the living creatures that God gave us in the first place. The fossil record shows that as many as 99 percent of all plant and animal species that ever lived may have become extinct since creation.

Chapter Three
The Genesis Flood

37. When did the Flood occur?

Archbishop James Ussher (1581–1658) gave a date of about 2350 BC for the Flood. He based this date on Genesis 11:10–26. This passage gives the years of family lineage from Shem, one of Noah's sons, to Abraham. And it is generally agreed by biblical scholars, both conservative and liberal, that Abraham lived about 2000 BC.

However, some creationists question Ussher's precise chronology. Some of the reasons are explained in *The Genesis Flood*, written by John Whitcomb and Henry Morris. For example, the term *begat* or *became the father of* sometimes refers to an ancestral relationship. Thus Genesis 11:12 may read "When Arphaxad had lived 35 years, he became the *grandfather*, *great grandfather*, or *ancestor* of Shelah (see also Luke 3:36). Hence, there may be additional unnamed generations in the list. One possible indication concerns Eber and Peleg who lived respectively 464 and 239 years (Gen. 11:16–19). The large difference in ages might indicate several intervening generations of decreasing life spans. If true, then the Flood date is earlier than 2350 BC. Even if several centuries are added, however, the Flood remains a fairly recent event, certainly within several thousand years. A generous "ballpark" estimate is that the Flood took place between 4500 and 6500 years ago.

The length of the Flood itself is a separate question. A century or more were involved in the ark construction (Gen. 5:32, 6:3, 7:6). The Flood event then lasted just over a year. Table 3-1 shows the timetable of the Deluge.

38. What is the Gilgamesh Epic?

In 1872, English archaeologist George Smith translated ancient Akkadian writing from several stone tablets found in the ruins of the Old Testament city of Nineveh. This ancient record told the Babylonian story of a great flood, now known as

Table 3-1. Timetable of the Genesis Flood using our present calendar. The dates are taken from Scripture (February 17 = "the seventh day of the second month," Genesis 7:11) although calendars have been altered over the years.

Month and Day	Flood Event	Scripture Reference
Feb. 17– March 28	40 days of rain	Gen. 7:11–23
Feb. 17– July 17	150 days of water covering the earth	Gen. 7:24–8:4
Oct. 1	Mountain tops become visible	Gen. 8:5
Nov. 9	Raven, dove sent out from the ark	Gen. 8:6–9
Nov. 16	Second dove sent out	Gen. 8:10–11
Nov. 23	Third dove sent out	Gen. 8:12
Jan. 1	Land appears	Gen. 8:13
Feb. 27	Departure from the ark	Gen. 8:16

the *Gilgamesh Epic,* named for an ancient hero. It is among the world's oldest known literature. Similar flood traditions have been found in many other ancient writings from the ancient Near East and elsewhere around the world.

Some liberal scholars have suggested that the Genesis Flood story was copied from the earlier Babylonian account. However, the Gilgamesh flood account is an unrealistic poem when compared with Scripture. A partial, loose translation of the Akkadian text reads (Pritchard, 1958, p. 66):

The gods produced a flood,
"Tear down this house, build a ship.
Her dimensions
Ten dozen cubits in each direction
Make it cube shaped, with six decks!"
In seven days the ship was launched
All the builders got on board
The weather was awesome
After seven days the storm ended.

One could not possibly ride out a flood in such a cube-shaped vessel! In contrast, the Genesis account of the ark and Flood are detailed, accurate history. The Gilgamesh Epic (2000–1700 BC) may have been composed earlier than Moses' account (1500 BC), and probably was based on the actual global Flood. However, the Genesis account is the far more reliable record of the event, and was given by divine inspiration.

39. Was the Flood worldwide?

Perhaps no Bible story is attacked more frequently than that of the Genesis Flood. Critics ask where all the water came from, where it eventually went, and what physical evidence remains today from such a worldwide catastrophe. Furthermore, how could a "floating zoo" be built in early times, and how could it possibly hold a pair of every species of animal? Of course, most critics have not closely studied the biblical account where clear answers to such questions are found.

In 1929, headlines proclaimed that archaeologist Sir Leonard Woolley had found evidence for the Genesis Flood. An eight-foot deposit of clay sediment was discovered in the ruins of the ancient city of Ur in lower Mesopotamia. There were human occupation remains both above and below this clay layer. From this evidence, many experts assumed that the biblical Flood was limited to this geographic region only. The sediment deposit indeed probably resulted from one of the periodic local floods of the area. However, the event of Noah's day was of much greater magnitude.

In 1999, divers found evidence of a submerged, former shoreline on the floor of the Black Sea, 550 feet below the present water level. On the bottom were found planks, posts, and the remains of a collapsed farm-size building. There also are fossils of freshwater clams in the sea bottom sediments, now replaced by living marine clams. Geologists theorize that the Black Sea, located between the Ukraine and Turkey, was once a small freshwater lake surrounded with towns. At the end of the ice age, melting glaciers raised the Mediterranean

Figure 3-1. A map of the Black Sea region of Eastern Europe. Floodwater is assumed to have poured into an original smaller Black Sea through the Bosporus Strait in the southwest corner from the Mediterranean Sea.

Sea level until it broke through a vast natural dam (Figure 3-1). This dam location, today's Bosporus Strait, separated the Mediterranean from the Black Sea. Many researchers assume that this massive, local flood drowned many shoreline cities. Survivors scattered outward in all directions, carrying the story of a great flood with them. A 1998 book titled *Noah's Flood*, written by William Ryan and Walter Pitman, concludes that the Black Sea event inspired the story of Noah.

There have certainly been destructive floods throughout earth history, including perhaps the Black Sea, but only one stands out as utterly unique. This was the worldwide Flood described in Genesis 6–8. The following is a partial list of evidences for a global Flood:

• Consider the language of Genesis 7:23: "So He destroyed all living things which were on the face of the ground: both man and cattle, creeping thing and bird of the air. They were destroyed from the earth. Only Noah and those who were with him in the ark remained alive." Either the Flood was world-wide, or else Scripture does not mean what it clearly states.

- The rainbow promise means little if the Flood was only local in extent (Genesis 9:13–16). After all, serious regional flood-ing occurs often in many places across the earth.

- Some have suggested that inhabitants of the early earth were limited to Mesopotamia. Therefore only that region, the "known world," was flooded. But why then was Noah com-manded to spend a century constructing the ark if it was not necessary? The Lord could have simply told his family to move away to higher ground.

- Seventy percent of earth's land surface is covered by thick layers of sedimentary rock. This rock type is water-deposited in its origin. In some locations this sedimentary rock is thou-sands of feet thick. Geologists explain these findings as due to many local floods and former seas. Instead however, one vast global Flood may be responsible for the great majority of sedimentary rock.

- The sedimentary rock layers hold an immense number of fossils. Many animal fossils, especially fish, appear con-torted, as if trapped in the midst of a struggle to escape silt and mud. Larger animals, including dinosaurs, appear to have been suddenly overwhelmed by a great catastrophe. Sediments accumulating in river deltas and mouths today do not preserve fossils in this way (Wheeler, 1975).

- Petrified tree trunks are sometimes found extending through several strata of rock. These *polystrate* fossils would be impossible if the separate rock layers accumulated slowly over tens of thousands of years.

- Graded bedding occurs in sedimentary layers when rock par-ticles are sorted out by size and density. In the past, this sorting was thought to be due to gradual gravity separation in quiet water. Some geologists now believe such strata are due to un-derwater turbidity currents. Such currents produce large-scale mudflows across the sea bottom. Turbidity currents move tremendous amounts of material, and can readily sort them out by size and density in the process (Question 82).

40. What was the source of the Floodwaters?

Genesis 7:11–12 describes two distinct sources of Floodwater. First, the *windows* or *floodgates* of heaven were opened to cause a steady downpour of rain for 40 days and nights. This was a unique precipitation event. Today there is a limited amount of moisture in the atmosphere. At most, a 2-inch equivalent depth of water could be squeezed from the air, worldwide. There may have been considerably more water in the atmosphere during preFlood history. One possible explanation is a *vapor canopy* which surrounded the early earth from the time of Adam to Noah. Such an invisible canopy could have provided immense amounts of rainwater.

The second source of water is described as the breaking forth of the *fountains* or *springs* of the deep. Groundwater is a plentiful resource today. Some of this groundwater is under pressure, resulting in springs, artesian wells, and geysers. At the time of Noah, there probably was considerably more groundwater, also under pressure. At God's command it was released upward upon the earth's surface.

In May, 1980, Mount St. Helens erupted in Washington State. The volcano's explosive power partially resulted from superheated water within the mountain. An initial earthquake dislodged the side of the mountain, exposing much hot water to the air. It instantly flashed to steam, causing the eruption. Mount St. Helens was thus somewhat equivalent to a giant boiler explosion. This event demonstrates the vast energy of heated groundwater. Multiple volcanic events may have accompanied the Genesis Flood. The Mount St. Helens event is further described in Question 49.

41. What is cavitation?

Cavitation is the rapid formation and collapse of low-pressure bubbles in water or other liquids. These bubbles occur when the fluid is agitated or moved rapidly. As a result, water pressure is reduced to its *vapor pressure* and bubbles form. The bubbles then collapse quickly when they reach regions of higher pressure. This rapid growth and collapse of tiny vapor *cavities* can cause extreme forces which pit and corrode nearby surfaces. Extensive erosion has occurred on the metal blades of water pumps, turbines, and ship propellers. On a smaller scale, cavitation is useful in ultrasonic cleaning devices. In some cases cavitation also produces high temperatures and flashes of light called *sonoluminescence*. The occasional clicking sound of "cracking" knuckles may also be a result of the cavitation process (Weiss, 2001).

The Glen Canyon Dam experienced a severe cavitation event in 1983. This large dam controls the Colorado River just above the Grand Canyon, and forms Lake Powell in Arizona and Utah. In Spring 1983, the lake was flooded by excessive snowmelt. During June the dam operators were forced to open a 40-foot diameter spillway to prevent the high water from overflowing the dam. As 32,000 cubic feet of water per second rushed through the manmade tunnel, the surrounding area rumbled and vibrated. Within just hours, the great force of the water eroded completely through the steel-reinforced concrete lining of the tunnel. Large chunks of concrete and pulverized rock were hurled outward with the water into the river below. The water tunnel was quickly closed and repairs made with 63,000 cubic feet of new reinforced concrete lining. This episode of near failure of the Glen Canyon Dam demonstrates the power of moving water and cavitation to rapidly erode solid rock beyond all predictions. Cavitation may have played a roll in large-scale erosion during the Genesis Flood. In this way, pre-existing rock and also newly formed rock layers were greatly worn down worldwide (Holroyd, 1990).

42. What are the catastrophic plate tectonic and hydroplate theories?

These are alternative models of major physical earth events surrounding the Genesis Flood. In the *catastrophic plate tec-*

tonic model, at the beginning of the Flood, gigantic slabs of ocean floor break lose and slide beneath the continents (Austin et al., 1994). These descending slabs deform the mantle and produce a great amount of heat by frictional movement. This heat causes rock melting which accelerates further movement of the oceanic slabs. Great plumes of molten mantle material, called magma, then rise to the earth's surface worldwide and erupt through fissures. This magma warms entire oceans and greatly increases evaporation and resulting precipitation. The rainfall contributes to the Genesis Flood downpour. This overall description of crustal movement is also called the *runaway subduction model* for the Flood.

The *hydroplate theory* assumes that the created earth held vast amounts of water in underground, interconnected chambers (Brown, 2001). When the Flood occurred, underground pressure caused this subterranean water to fracture overlying rock layers. As the earth's crust was ripped open worldwide, hot ground water flashed to steam and shot upward. Some plumes of gaseous vapor rose 70 miles above the earth. Accompanying fountains of liquid water also erupted, accompanied by tidal waves 10,000 feet high. These catastrophic events triggered the biblical Deluge.

Both ideas briefly outlined here are possible scenarios for the great Flood. Both models also raise questions as to the required forces and energies involved. There will be continued development and refining of these possible Flood models, as well as others. For example, one alternative approach is called the "impacts and vertical tectonics model" (Oard, 2002). Another is called the Creation/Curse/Catastrophe (CCC) model (Gentet, 2000).

43. Was Mount Everest covered by the Flood?

According to Genesis 7:19–20, every hill and mountain on earth was completely covered by the floodwaters. As evidence, Mount Everest has a wide band of marine limestone near its summit. The sedimentary rock had its origin beneath water, and is present in many mountain ranges. Igneous and metamorphic rock masses are also interspersed within mountains. Marine fossils such as shells and coral are common on the earth's high mountain summits. According to Psalm 104:7–9, many high elevations were supernaturally thrust upward at the conclusion of the Flood as the ocean basins sank downward (see Question 53),

> At Thy rebuke they [waters] fled;
> At the sound of Thy thunder they hurried away.
> The mountains rose; the valleys sank down
> To the place which Thou didst establish for them.
> Thou didst set a boundary that they may not pass over;
> That they may not return to cover the earth.
>   (New American Standard Bible)

Although the material that makes up Mount Everest was indeed covered by the floodwaters, the mountain itself may not have existed until after the Flood. As the earth's crust was supernaturally thrust upward, it carried underwater sediment along with it. Modern mountain ranges likely originated at this time. Genesis 7:19 explains that during the great Flood, all the high hills and peaks existing at that time were covered. Today's highest mountains, however, may be postFlood features, far higher than preFlood mountains.

44. Was the ark sufficiently large to hold all the animals?

Skeptics have attacked the idea of a "floating zoo" that somehow held all of the kinds of animals. However, such skeptics have seldom taken the time to study the biblical account. First, consider the capacity of the ark (Gen. 6:15–16). Taking a cubit as 18 inches, the floor area of the ark with its three decks totals just over 100,000 square feet (Figure 3-2). This is equivalent to 50 full size American homes. The volume of the ark totals over 1.5 million cubic feet, equal to the capacity of more than 530 railroad boxcars.

How many total animals were on board the ark? This is a difficult question because the number of distinct species living today is poorly known, and is variously estimated between 40–80 million (Question 36). Let us consider living creatures as percentages of the estimated total. They can be divided into the

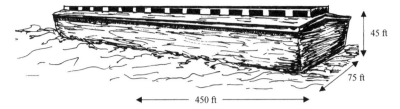

Figure 3-2. An illustration of the Ark. For the dimensions shown, a cubit is assumed to equal 18 inches.

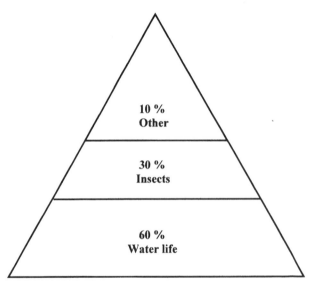

Figure 3-3. The known species of animals living upon the earth, listed by percentages of the total.

categories shown in Figure 3-3. The majority of all known animal species, about 60 percent of the total, live in water. These freshwater and marine animals were not brought on board the ark. Many billions died in the Flood as attested by the fossil record. Challenges to their life included turbulence, sediment, and the mixing of salt and fresh water. Nevertheless, representatives survived as shown by present-day sea life. Next in abundance, thirty percent of all known life forms are in the insect category. Many of these probably were brought on board the ark, taking up little space. Others could have survived the Flood in the form of eggs, perhaps attached to floating debris.

The final 10 percent of known species includes the birds and mammals. One estimate puts 8,000 distinct animals in this category. Including males and females, the total is then 16,000 (Woodmorappe, 1996). This number refers to the biblical *kinds*, not the narrower biological *species*. For example, a pair of wolf-like animals could have represented the *dog* kind. In the years following the Flood, all the dog varieties could develop from this original pair, as well as wolves, foxes, coyotes and dingoes. The DNA makeup of wolves and domestic dogs is almost identical (Lange, 2002). This possible development of new species is called *speciation*, and is not macroscopic evolution. Instead, it describes the potential for variation created *within* the biblical kinds. With the numbers suggested here, there was indeed adequate room on the ark for the creatures together with their food supply, and also Noah's family.

45. Has Noah's Ark been found?

Over the years there have been many intriguing reports of ark discoveries on Mount Ararat, located in modern Turkey. Recent decades have seen dozens of expeditions to this remote area. The results have included many disappointments, some hoaxes, and also some glimmers of hope. Table 3-2 lists some representative expeditions from past years. Reports of recovered physical evidence from Noah's ark, along with indistinct photographs, remain doubtful. For example, wood returned from an altitude of 14,000 foot by French explorer Fernand Navarra in 1955 has been carbon dated around 700 A.D., too recent for ark material.

One possible conclusion is that the ark has indeed been found by several expeditions in previous centuries but is presently lost. The Jewish historian Josephus, writing about the Ararat region in the first century AD, states " . . . for the ark being saved in that place, its remains are shown there by the inhabitants to this day" (Josephus, 1883). Josephus also quoted Berassus, a Chaldean priest from the third century BC, who recorded that "there is still some part of this ship in Armenia at the mountain of the Cardyaens; and some people carry off

Table 3-2. A summary of modern searches for Noah's Ark.

Date	Name	Reported Findings
1829	Fredrich Parrot	Wood
1840	Avalanche team	Prow of a ship jutting from a lake of ice
1887	Persian archbishop	An ark with dark red wood
1916	Russian soldiers	An ark, as "long as a city block"
1952	George J. Greene	Prow of a ship
1950s	Ferdinand Navarra	Hand-tooled wood fragment
Recent	John Morris, John Montgomery, Jim Irwin, and others	No conclusive evidence found

pieces of the bitumen, which they take away, and use chiefly as amulets for the advertising of mischiefs." A thousand years after Josephus, the explorer Marco Polo (1254–1324) described Mount Ararat: "In the central part of Armenia stands an exceedingly large and high mountain, upon which, it is said, the ark of Noah rested, and for this reason it is termed the Mountain of the Ark."

The Ararat region of Turkey borders Iran and Russia where it is politically difficult and dangerous to travel. Modern ark searchers have had to deal with furious blizzards, avalanches, lightning, thieves, wild dogs, and political revolutions! One must question the wisdom of ark exploration under these dangerous conditions. Its possible discovery in our day would be of great interest and encouragement to believers. However, the ark's value as a testimony to skeptics is doubtful. A host of archaeological finds and fulfilled prophecy already point to the absolute reliability of Scripture, yet many people remain willfully and stubbornly unconvinced of its biblical truth.

According to Genesis 8:4 the ark came to rest on the *mountains* of Ararat, a plural noun. In earlier centuries, Ararat also was the name of a country located in parts of Eastern Turkey and Armenia. Ancient Ararat included the Caucasus Mountains, so there are numerous places where the ark may have settled. Therefore, it is possible that today's Mount Ararat is not the actual ark landing site. Wherever the location, the ark may be presently encased in ice, may have disintegrated, or alternatively may be found again in the near future. Regardless, physical ark evidence is not needed in order to accept the Flood account. Faith, a confident trust in things unseen, is a foundational part of Christianity.

46. Have human artifacts been found in rocks and coal?

It is commonly thought that mankind has existed during only the most recent period of earth history. Human civilization often is said to be limited to less than 100,000 years, contrasting with a 4.6 billion-year-old earth. Therefore any cultural implements or human remains should be limited to the topmost rock layers of earth, within the late Cenozoic era (Table 2-1). However, a large collection of "out of place" human artifacts, footprints, and bones has accumulated over time. These objects variously have been found during excavations, mining, and well drilling operations.

The unusual finds have often been poorly recorded and documented because their significance was not realized at the time. Also, such finds are discounted outright by geologists as hoaxes or mistakes. However, a single verified cultural object found in the wrong place is sufficient to raise fundamental questions about the gradual formation of geologic strata long before man's existence. The following list gives some out-of-place artifacts, many found in past centuries (Peterson, 2002; Chittick, 1997).

- 1826: A 94 foot well was dug in Cincinnati, Ohio. At the bottom was found a tree stump with an iron ax wedge embedded in it. Its age was estimated at 75,000 years. However, our early ancestors are not thought to have used metal tools.
- 1867: A silver mine in Gilman, Colorado produced human bones and also a copper arrowhead. The remains were embedded within a vein of silver metal, 400 feet deep and dated at 135 million years old.
- 1889: A 1.5 inch doll was found during the drilling of a 320-foot well in Nampa, Idaho (Gentet and Lain, 1999). The

doll is made of clay and quartz, and shows detailed artistic decoration. The layer in which the doll was found is assumed to be about 300,000 years old. This intriguing Nampa Doll is on permanent exhibit at the Idaho State Historical Society in Boise.

- In Morrisonville, Illinois, a ten-inch gold chain was found within a lump of coal. The coal deposit was estimated at 300 million years old.
- A geode (hollow rock) from Olancha, California contained a mysterious spark plug-like device. Geologists have dated the geode at 500,000 years old (Chittick, 1997).

These few items represent a long list of unusual objects found within the earth. Many such finds are undoubtedly natural objects with unusual shapes. In other cases, however, they are likely preFlood materials that were buried by Flood sediments. The burden is on geologists to explain these significant "out of place" mysteries of the earth. William Corliss has catalogued additional artifacts in a series of books (1991). These resources, available in many libraries, are a fascinating compilation of unexplained anomalies in nature.

47. How did the Grand Canyon form?

Arizona's Grand Canyon is often called a *monument to time*. In the usual story, the first stage of formation involved the accumulation of various sedimentary layers over a period of 300 million years when shallow seas covered the region. Later the region was gradually raised, then eroded by the Colorado River. Geologists believe there were a series of downcutting pulses, the result of periodic uplifts of the area and the variable resistance of sedimentary rock types. Major uncertainties of this model include precipitation and erosion rates, stages of uplift, and the entire time scale involved.

Creationists have an entirely different view of the formation of the Grand Canyon. As might be expected, the story involves catastrophism and a short time scale. It is suggested that the sedimentary layers, totaling more than a mile in thickness, were deposited during the Genesis Flood event. Storm surges,

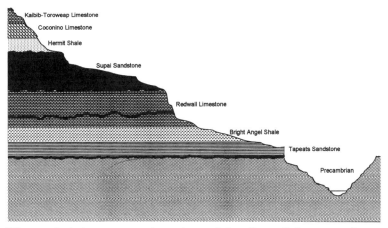

Figure 3-4. A cross section view of the Grand Canyon showing sedimentary layers and fossil content, not to scale. The Colorado River is seen at the very bottom of the canyon.

lunar tidal effects, and density sorting of sediments led to the observed multiple layers (Figure 3-4). Then in the centuries directly following the Flood, there was a colder period of climate across the earth (Question 51). During this period much snow and ice were deposited upon the North America continent and elsewhere. When this ice age finally ended, many large inland lakes resulted. The sites of these former lakes can still be seen in large valleys in the western states.

There are alternate creationist theories on the formation of the Grand Canyon. Some suggest that the canyon formed at the end of the Flood as the waters rushed off the North American Continent (Oard, 2001). Others suggest that a large post-Flood lake existed near the eastern end of today's Grand Canyon, sometimes called *Grand* or *Canyonlands Lake* (Figure 3-5). It may have been held in place by a vast ice dam. When this dam eventually broke or melted through, the entire lake then rushed across northern Arizona, rapidly scouring out the Grand Canyon system. An immense amount of eroded rock and mud debris was scattered outward across Nevada and southern California. In this interpretation, the present-day Colorado River is a mere trickle compared to the

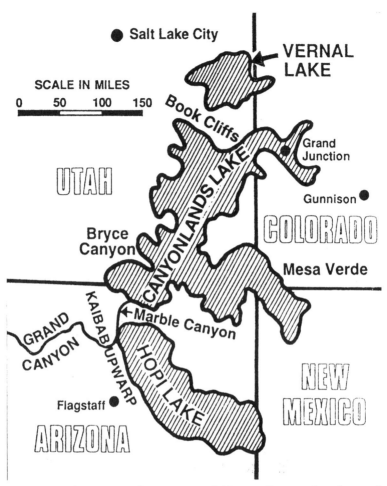

Figure 3-5. Former locations of Hopi, Canyonlands, and Vernal Lakes on the Colorado Plateau. These lakes may have breached their dams, causing catastrophic drainage and erosion of Grand Canyon (Austin, 1994).

torrents of water that rapidly cut the majestic canyon. Such a large-scale flooding event is an amazing picture to contemplate.

In recent years, many geologists have recognized the rapid formation of the Grand Canyon. Its assumed age has been reduced by some from over 50 million years to less than one million years (Perkins, 2000). New evidence for catastrophic formation will probably reduce this time still further, bringing it closer to the creationist view.

I will close this discussion with a humorous story told by Pastor Charles Swindoll. Two men were standing at the edge of the Grand Canyon. Seeing the great depth, one man said, "This is the work of God." The other man said, "Watch, this is the first time I ever spit a mile." I guess it is all how you look at things!

48. What are the Channeled Scablands?

This is a region of eastern Washington State marked by large-scale water erosion. Fine-grained sediment covers volcanic basalt throughout the area. Many river channels 50–100 feet deep or greater have been cut through the soil and into the underlying hard basalt layer. There are also abundant canyons and former waterfalls. The region is quite dry today, lacking sufficient rain for permanent streams in most valleys. In 1923, geologist J. Harlen Bretz first proposed a catastrophic flood origin for the Channeled Scablands. For the next half-century, most geologists rejected his idea in favor of slow, gradual erosion. By the 1960s, however, virtually everyone accepted a rapid erosion event. This rugged 3000 square mile Columbia Plateau region bears testimony to a dramatic past.

Toward the close of the Ice Age, glacial ice blocked the release of melt water from nearby western Montana. Lake Missoula formed as a result, and was half as large as Lake Michigan is today. When the great ice dam eventually broke through, 500 cubic miles (2000 km³) of water swept westward across Washington State in one of North America's greatest regional floods. The water flowed over the land at the rate of up to 17 million cubic feet per second, easily moving 40-foot boulders along its path. This catastrophic event is sometimes called the Spokane or Lake Missoula Flood. There remain today giant streambed ripple marks, up to 22 feet high and 425 feet long. A much smaller version of these ripple marks is often found beneath shallow moving water in streams and lakes. Portions of the Grand Coulee gorge were largely excavated in just days as the giant wall of floodwater rushed onward to the sea. This canyon is 50 miles (80 km) long, one to six miles wide, 900 feet (275m) deep, and is chiseled directly through solid basalt and granite.

Recognition of this local Northwest flood illustrates the trend toward catastrophic thinking in current geology. No longer is the *present* always thought to be the key to the *past*. Instead the earth has experienced quiet periods divided by major, rapid changes. The channeled scablands are a powerful testimony to the rapid work of water erosion.

Scabland-type areas and former lake basins have also been found on the surface of the planet Mars. It is not known whether similar large-scale water or lava flooding may have occurred there in the past. Mars holds many mysteries including its strange erosion marks.

49. What has Mount Saint Helens taught us?

On Sunday morning, May 18, 1980, Mount St. Helens erupted. The volcanic blast leveled trees within a 400-square-kilometer area of southwestern Washington State. The resulting dust and ash gave color to sunsets across North America for weeks. Measurable dust deposits were reported as far away as Oklahoma and Minnesota. This event has provided excellent opportunities to study catastrophic geologic change. The following list gives some of the creationist implications of the Mount St. Helens event (Austin, 1994).

- The volcanic debri called *tephra* formed multiple layers of strata, 600 feet thick in places. This shows that many stratification layers can form very quickly.

- Mud and debris blocked the nearby Toutle River. The trapped water quickly eroded through solid rock to form a new drainage path. Gritty water, especially, can cut through solid rock in little time.

- Thousands of large logs were deposited in nearby Spirit Lake. Later they became waterlogged and sank. Many of these displaced trees now are found to be *implanted* on the bottom of the lake in an upright position, as if they grew there. This has major implications for other geologic puzzles (see Question 65).

- Great amounts of bark and other tree debris have settled to the bottom of Spirit Lake. This material has the composition and texture of peat, usually found in bogs. Ongoing studies are monitoring the expected change of these lake deposits to a form of coal. This rapid accumulation of material challenges the usual assumption that peat and coal formation requires a vast time period.

- When Mount St. Helens erupted it was assumed that vegetation and wildlife in the region would be extinguished, perhaps for centuries. President Jimmy Carter reported that "the moon looks like a golf course" compared to the Mount St. Helens area. Just decades later, however, the area again flourishes with a great variety of plants and animals. The living world clearly was created with the ability to adapt and thrive in disturbed environments. This displays a designed strength and healthiness to ecosystems.

- The explosive nature of Mount St. Helens was largely due to superheated ground water. Water-rich magma was trapped within the mountain. An earthquake finally caused the north slope of the mountain to slide downward, reducing pressure on the magma. Its water component then flashed to steam, triggering the eruption, similar to a boiler explosion. This process shows the power of unleashed ground water with profound implications for the Genesis Flood event. Large numbers of volcanoes may have accompanied the global Flood.

50. How did animals reach Australia after the Flood?

Australia displays a unique assortment of plants and animals. These include the kangaroo, platypus, koala, kookaburra, waddy tree, and Tasmanian devil. The platypus is so unusual with its webbed feet, duck bill, and flat tail that initial reports

Figure 3-6. The darker area represents the land bridge which once connected Siberia with Alaska.

of the creature in the 1700s were doubted by biologists. Skeptics claimed that a taxidermist had sewn parts of different animals together as a hoax! But the platypus is real, a unique semi-aquatic egg-laying mammal.

Before the time of the Genesis Flood, we do not know which regions of the earth these particular plants and animals inhabited. The positions and the number of continents themselves have changed greatly from preFlood days. Scattered fossils of Australia-type animals are found in other lands, but such finds are rare. After the Flood, probably in connection with the Ice Age (see Question 51), ocean levels dropped about 200 feet (61 m). This exposed the continental shelves. These are submerged areas beyond the present coastlines of the world. There are also many relatively shallow "pathways" beneath the seas. Figure 3-6 shows the land bridge which once connected Siberia and Alaska, now the Bering Strait. Similar land bridges existed between Asia and Australia. Today the region is covered by seas a few hundred meters deep, called the Sunda and Sahul sea shelves. With lower ocean levels during the Ice Age, a land bridge hundreds of miles wide could thus have extended between the Northern and Southern Hemispheres. As animals multiplied in the years following the Flood, these land bridges provided an efficient means of dispersion as animals migrated to remote parts of the earth. There is a second, alternate possibility for the postFlood delivery of animals to Australia. Following the Babel dispersion of Genesis 11, people may have brought animals with them to Australia and elsewhere around the planet. The impact of plant and animal *cultural* distribution by people continues in our own day. An additional possibility for animal distribution is transport on large floating log mats that probably existed for years following the Flood.

The particular plants and animals of Australia were able to survive and prosper because of a climate and habitat that ideally suited them. In a similar way the Arctic region, the tropics, and the deserts each have their own unique combination of thriving plants and animals. The plant and animal life of Australia seems particularly exotic since most people only see these creatures in zoos. They were a part of God's original creation and still remain for our enjoyment and wonder today.

51. Was there an ice age?

The Swiss naturalist Louis Agassiz first popularized ice age evidence in the 1830s–1840s. Glacial features from the past that Agassiz recognized include:
- Erratic, out-of-place boulders transported by ice.
- Unsorted gravel deposits.
- Rock abrasions and varves.
- Unusual landforms including kettle lakes, kames, moraines, drumlins, and eskers.
- Historical changes in the direction of flow of rivers.
- A compression of the land surface due to heavy overlying ice.
- Historical lowering of the sea level.

Geologists often speak of several distinct ice ages occurring about 2 billion, 600 million, 250 million, and 2 million years ago. The most recent ice age is thought to have had many cycles of warm and cool climate, extending over perhaps 2.5 million years and ending quite recently. The earth is supposedly experiencing a short interglacial period today. Such evidence is largely determined from ice cores and sea floor sediments.

The particular ice episode said to have occurred 600 million years ago is emphasized as an extremely cold period on earth, lasting 100 million years. The average temperature is thought to have dropped to −58°F (−50°C), killing most life on earth. The evidence is based on glacial debri found in remote areas believed to have been at low latitudes at the time. Further data indicates that after this harsh ice age, the earth's average temperature then rapidly increased in one hundred years or so, perhaps to 122°F (50°C), baking the earth's surface (Hoffman and Schrag, 2000). Such a rapid climate change within decades is disturbing to scientists since its cause is unknown.

Many mechanisms have been suggested as ice age triggers, none of them convincing:

• A cooler sun in the past.
• An asteroid impact or volcano which shaded the sun with atmospheric dust.
• Removal of carbon dioxide from the earth's atmosphere.
• A change in the earth's solar orbit or a change in the tilt of earth's rotation axis.

Creationists have a *better idea* to explain a cooler climate (Oard, 1990). They describe a single ice age in postFlood times, just 3,000–5,000 years ago. Evidence that is often interpreted in terms of distinct ice ages may actually point to recessions and advances of a single event. The Flood itself triggered the Ice Age. Following this Flood, the oceans held water that had been warmed from tectonic and volcanic activity. This oceanic warming resulted in increased evaporation. On the land, especially in polar regions, the resulting precipitation accumulated rapidly as snow and ice. Just two conditions actually are needed to cause an ice age, high precipitation and cool summer seasons. Both occurred in the postFlood centuries.

Ice sheets grew due to a "perpetual winter." In North America the ice covered Canada and the upper Midwest. Northern Europe also was blanketed in thick ice. In the Southern Hemisphere, Tasmania was largely enveloped by glaciation. Eventually, the oceans cooled and evaporation diminished to its present rate. Other warming factors included the regrowth of forests and increasing carbon dioxide amounts in the atmosphere. In this creation view, there will not be another ice age because the Flood was a unique, one-time event.

52. Were mammoths flash-frozen?

Woolly mammoths looked somewhat like shaggy elephants. They had long, graceful tusks that curved outward and upward. Coarse hair protected them from a cold climate. There are probably more than 5 million woolly mammoth remains buried in Siberia and Alaska. During the 18th and 19th centuries, 40,000–60,000 fossil mammoth tusks were collected in Siberia alone. These ivory tusks entered the world economic market and became billiard balls, piano keys, and other products. Less numerous than mammoths of North America were the mastodons which had a different tooth structure. Mastodon teeth were low-crowned and well suited for grazing.

In the creation view, these creatures survived the great Flood on board the ark. Then in the postFlood years they multiplied greatly in northern regions. The Ice Age which followed was a difficult time for mastodons and mammoths. Many fossil specimens appear to have died of starvation or in dust storms (Oard, 2000). On rare occasions, mammoth remains appear to have been very rapidly frozen at death, or *flash-frozen*. Much publicity has been given to the finding of fresh plants within the stomachs of icy mammoths. These types of remains, however, are highly unusual. In the few cases where undigested, unspoiled internal vegetation is

Figure 3-7. "Dima," a frozen baby mammoth found in 1977 in Siberia. It weighed 200 pounds (90 kg), the size of a large dog (Blount and Crowley, 2001).

found, it may be explained by severe ice age conditions. Most mammoths do not appear to have been flash-frozen.

Mammoths are commonly said to have died out about 10,000 years ago from some unknown cause. The biblical ice age advances this date of extinction to only about 4,000 years ago in postFlood years. In fact, until about 3,800 years ago, according to C-14 dating, woolly mammoths are known to have lived on Wrangel Island, off the coast of Siberia. In addition to the cold climate, people may have hunted the last mammoths to extinction. On several occasions, spear points are found associated with mammoth remains. Musk-oxen populations, which existed together with the Arctic mammoths, still live today.

In 1977, gold prospectors found a complete baby mammoth frozen in Siberian tundra (Figure 3-7). Named *Dima*, it is now on display at the University of Leningrad, complete with its delicate 2-foot-long (60 cm) trunk. Also, in 1999, a full-size mammoth was discovered encased in mud and ice, again in Siberia. Blood studies show a close kinship with modern Indian elephants.

53. Does Psalm 104 refer to Flood events?

This question concerns the text of Psalm 104:6–9. It describes water initially standing above the mountains, then fleeing at God's command. The retreating waters are said to flow down into great valleys, or the ocean basins. The present-day sea-coasts are described as boundaries which prevent the water from returning again to cover the land.

Psalm 104 deals with both the original creation event (verses 1–5), and earth history (verses 6–35). Some scholars limit the Psalm 104:6–9 verses to the original creation instead of the Noahic Flood. However, they face two major problems. *First*, verses 6–8 describe retreating waters flowing over the mountains. But the original waters of Genesis 1:2 did not cover previously existing mountains. In fact, mountains are not mentioned in Genesis 1, but they are described in the Flood account (Gen. 7:19). *Second*, the original seas were not bound by a permanent decree that they would not again cover the earth (Psalm 104:9). Instead, this clearly is the *rainbow covenant* of Genesis 9:15–16.

It appears that Psalm 104:6–9 is indeed a Genesis Flood description. This is the interpretation of scholars such as J. A. Alexander, Bruce Waltke, and John Whitcomb. There are other parallel passages that similarly telescope together creation and Flood descriptions. These include Job 38:10–11, Proverbs 8:29, Jeremiah 5:22, and 2 Peter 3:5–6. Psalm 104 is sometimes called the "Ecologist's Psalm" for its detailed descriptions of animals, vegetation, and the overall harmony of nature.

Chapter Four
On and Beneath Earth's Surface

54. What are the basic categories of rocks?

Rocks are divided into three broad categories based on their formation. First, *igneous* rocks occur when molten material cools. The word comes from the Latin term for fire, as in *ignite* and *ignition*. Igneous examples include the two most abundant rocks in the earth's crust, granite and basalt. The second category, *metamorphic* rocks are pre-existing rocks which have been altered by underground pressure, chemicals, and heat. The word metamorphic means "change," similar to the metamorphosis of the caterpillar into a butterfly. Metamorphic rock examples include marble and slate that originally were limestone and shale.

The third basic rock category is *sedimentary*. In this case, sediment from weathered rocks is carried by water to a pond or lake where it settles and may eventually dry out. Circulating ground water may later carry dissolved minerals which cement or *lithify* the rock. Sedimentary rock may also form directly under water. It is characterized by horizontal layers, or *stratification*, as observed in the walls of the Grand Canyon, and in many places where roads have been cut through rock formations. Common sedimentary examples include limestone, sandstone, shale, and conglomerate.

The total amounts of rock types in the earth's crust are estimated as
- igneous   67%
- metamorphic 25%
- sedimentary   8%

Although sedimentary rock does not dominate the list, it is the rock most often seen. Sedimentary strata are spread across the topmost land surface of the earth, somewhat like thick layers of paint, often hundreds of feet thick, and sometimes miles in depth. When did all this sedimentary rock originate? The conventional view is a very slow formation, averaging just mil-

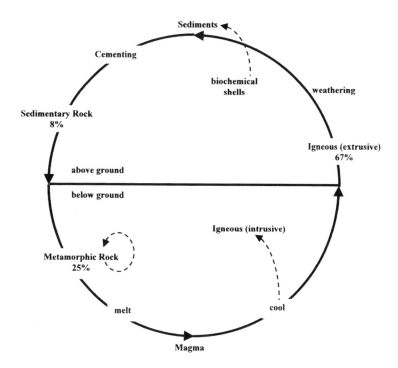

Figure 4-1. An illustration of the rock cycle. Dotted lines with arrows show several possible changes. The solid horizontal line separates rocks that form below ground (intrusive) and at the earth's surface (extrusive).

limeters of depth in a century. On a small scale it probably forms continually upon the earth. However, the great amounts of existing sedimentary rock may well have originated during the worldwide Flood.

Figure 4-1 illustrates the *rock cycle*. It shows how rocks can be transformed between the three basic types. Rock material can work its way around the outside of the circle, or take a "shortcut" through the center. For example, igneous rock can be directly remelted to magma. Also, metamorphic rock can directly weather to become loose sediments. Obviously, rocks are not "forever." They are part of the dynamic, changing earth.

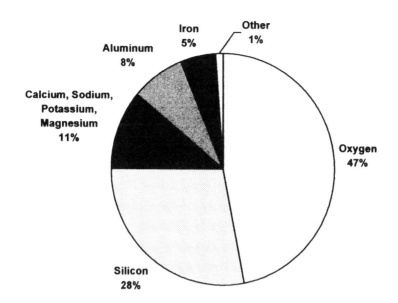

Figure 4-2. The major elements which comprise the earth's solid crust. Approximate percentages of the total are shown, by weight. The "other" category includes all the remaining elements found in the periodic table.

55. What is special about sand?

Until recent decades there was *nothing* special known about sand. It is an extremely plentiful resource and is not impressive in appearance. Sand has served mankind mainly as a building component in concrete and plaster. When raised to its high melting temperature of about 2600°C (4712°F), pure sand also becomes the major component of glass. Sand largely consists of silicon dioxide, SiO_2, also called silica or quartz. Silicon is the second most abundant element in the earth's crust, after oxygen (Figure 4-2). Nevertheless, the present technological era has found silicon to be a very special material called an electrical *semiconductor*. This means that the movement of electrical current through a pure silicon crystal can be easily controlled or changed by adding very small amounts of *doping* elements. Because of this valuable property, silicon has become a central component in solid state electronics. This field of technology dates from about 1949 when the first silicon transistor was made, replacing the bulky vacuum tube. A second valuable property of silicon is its *piezoelectric* behavior. A quartz crystal can be made to vibrate at a very precise frequency, while it also generates a small voltage. Typical frequencies range between 10 thousand and 10 million cycles per second, or hertz. Microscopic integrated circuits, including those inside digital watches, telephones, radios, and computers, incorporate silicon components. Electronic advancements using silicon chips and other semiconductors are rapidly advancing and new applications appear to be almost boundless. One of the earth's most common materials, silicon, has thus opened vast new fields for study and application.

A further technical use of silicon is in fiber optics. The fibers are made of very pure glass, thinner than a strand of hair. Light signals are passed through the fiber, carrying 250,000 times as much data as a copper wire. Pure glass is the best known transmitter of information. Cable companies have installed many millions of miles of fiber optics across the U.S.

The unique electrical and optical properties of silicon were part of the original design of the Creation. The potential benefits of silicon technology simply waited for modern technology to "catch up." One wonders about the host of other useful designs all around us, planned by the Lord, that await discovery.

56. Where do diamonds come from?

Brilliant diamonds captivate everyone. They have the greatest hardness of any mineral, a result of strong covalent chemical bonds between carbon atoms. Other natural forms of pure carbon include graphite, and tiny spheres called buckyballs. Diamonds are thought to crystallize under great pressure within the earth's upper mantle, about 90 miles (150 km) underground. Then they eventually are carried to the surface by upwelling magma. The igneous mineral kimberlite, or "blue ground," often contains diamonds. The kimberlite is found in solidified vertical "pipes." One of the largest manmade holes on earth is a mined-out diamond pipe 600 meters across and a kilometer deep, located in South Africa. Diamonds are also found in Zaire, Brazil, Russia, and in some U.S. western states.

There is a common assumption that diamonds formed millions of years ago. However, this view is challenged by research. Studies of synthetic diamonds show that newly formed specimens often contain nitrogen atoms as an impurity. This embedded nitrogen absorbs light and gives fresh diamonds a brown color. Over time, 10^3–10^4 years, it is thought that the individual nitrogen atoms migrate and bond together, and the diamond then clears. High temperatures are found to accelerate this clearing process (Figure 4-3).

If natural diamonds truly are ancient, they should all be clear by now. After all, the diamonds are assumed to be trapped within high pressure, high temperature mineral pipes for eons of time. However, *brown* natural diamonds are occasionally found with still-isolated nitrogen atoms within them. A British study concluded that such diamonds, "must have been ejected to the surface of the earth within 50 years of their formation—a very short time scale geologically" (Davies, 1981). In other words, these brown diamonds must have been *rapidly* brought to the earth's surface by tectonic activity. They are not necessarily ancient in age after all.

57. How much gold is in the world?

Gold was created with many unique properties. Its surface is virtually indestructible by chemical reactions. Gold does not rust, tarnish, or corrode. The yellow metal also is extremely malleable. Just one ounce of gold can be stretched into a wire 50 miles long, becoming finer than a strand of hair. There are traces of gold circuitry within many digital watches, cell phones, and calculators. Two metals, silver and gold, are found to be the best conductors of electricity. Gold's shiny, reflecting surface also provides a protective heat shield for space vehicles.

Gold is a rare element. In fact, the entire world's recovered supply could be collected into a single block just 18 yards (16.5 meters) on each side! This amount includes all the known coins, jewelry, bullion, and industrial gold. Such a concentrated cube would weigh 100,000 tons and would quickly sink directly into the earth! There is a far greater amount of unmined gold dissolved in the world's oceans, more than ten million tons, but it cannot easily be recovered.

The biblical land of Havilah was an early source of gold according to Genesis 2:11. Some of this may have been "placer" gold that had accumulated along the river Pishon. Placer gold is eroded from its source, then transported and deposited by water. The geographic locations of Havilah and Pishon are not known today. Such early geographic localities were erased completely by the Genesis Flood destruction.

In David and Solomon's day, gold was collected in great abundance to decorate the first Jewish temple at Jerusalem. The recorded quantities are impressive. There were 100,000 talents of gold, each talent weighing about 75 pounds (1 Chronicles 22:14). This amount of gold can be expressed several ways:

- 100,000 talents
- 7,500,000 pounds
- 3,750 tons
- 375 10-ton truckloads

The world's present production, distribution, and supply of gold is accurately known and catalogued. Ancient gold supplies have been traded, fought over, and remelted, but never destroyed. The historical figures on the production of gold are estimated by the Gold Information Center of New York as follows,

- Early times–1400: 50 tons
- 1400–1900: 5,500 tons
- 1900s: 95,000 tons

These figures reveal an intriguing mystery (DeYoung, 1988; Millard 2002). The quantity of gold described in the Old Testament temple is 75 times more than has been accounted for in the current inventory from early times, 3,750 tons versus just 50 tons. In fact, Solomon's recorded accumulation of gold amounts to nearly 4 percent of the present world supply. Annual additions of gold to Solomon's treasury may well double this discrepancy to 8 percent or more (1 Kings 10: 14).

To resolve this substantial historical discrepancy in gold amounts, one has several options. *First* a biblical talent of weight may have been less than the assumed 75 pounds. However, a talent was the largest weight standard of early Hebrews, and apparently was a full burden for a man to carry (2 Kings 5: 23). It was probably not less than 70–75 pounds, and maybe more. *Second*, Solomon's gold may have been an impure, diluted form of the metal. This is doubtful, however, since Old Testament people were proficient in the alloying and purifying of metals. As early as Genesis 4:22, Adam's descendant named Tubal-Cain is described as a metallurgist. There were at least six different Hebrew words for gold, and the temple reference in Chronicles is to pure, refined gold with a golden surface luster. As a *third* option, the published supply of the world's recovered gold may be seriously in error by several percent, or thousands of tons. In this case more than 3,700 tons of gold have been hidden, lost, or wrongly categorized. Perhaps the account books of gold need to be audited! This is an intriguing mystery in which biblical data reveals useful information that modern technology has overlooked.

58. How do coal, oil, and gas form?

Fossil fuels are thought to result largely from the burial and compaction of plant and animal material at high temperatures and pressures. Such fuel therefore consists of stored solar energy from the past, mainly carbon. A microscopic look at coal often reveals the outlines of compressed tropical bark, wood, and leaves. The standard view of coal formation involves the deposition of organic plant material in a swamp setting over a very long time period. Swamp water is deficient in oxygen so the submerged plants are preserved instead of de-

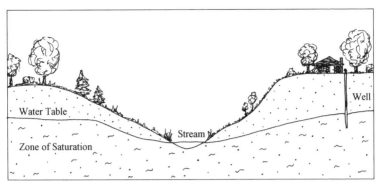

Figure 4-4. A diagram of the water table, the upper boundary of the underground region that is saturated with water.

composed. The organic material may be slowly transformed through the metamorphic stages of peat, lignite, bituminous, and finally anthracite coal. The Carboniferous period of the Paleozoic era is said to be the greatest coal-producing time span, occurring between about 280–310 million years ago.

The creationist view pictures the preFlood world as a time of lush tropical plant growth worldwide. Much of this vegetation then was converted into fossil fuel after rapid burial during the Genesis Flood. Centuries of accumulated plant and tree growth, worldwide, can account for all the fossil fuel reserves. This includes the earth's estimated seven trillion tons of coal. However, it is not certain that all fossil fuel has a plant origin. Underground microbial activity may also produce oil and gas. Much of the earth's natural gas, methane (CH_4), also may be inorganic in its origin. For example, ice-like deposits of *methane hydrates* are found scattered across the deep ocean floor. This material could be a major future source of methane or natural gas. These hydrates have formed from a precipitation process in seawater. Research continues on other inorganic processes which might produce hydrocarbons.

59. What is the water table?

This name is given to the upper boundary of underground water. The water table is usually not flat, but instead rises and falls with the land surface above (Figure 4-4). The water table becomes visible as the surface of a pond, or lake. However, it is usually tens of feet beneath the ground surface, and may be hundreds of feet deep in some locations. There is at least thirty times more water underground than in all of the world's surface rivers and lakes combined (Table 5-1).

Usually there is not an open cavity for underground water. Instead, countless tiny pores and cracks in the gravels and bedrock are filled with water. Ground water extends downward to a depth of a mile or more, where the underlying rock foundation becomes greatly compressed by pressure and pore spaces are closed. Most underground water slowly moves laterally to lower levels due to gravity. It may then eventually emerge to supply a river, lake, or sea. Water may also exit as a surface spring or it may be pumped upward from a drilled well. In deserts an oasis appears when the water table is drawn naturally toward the surface by capillary action. Groundwater is recharged by rain or snow; the water table may rise and fall with the seasons.

The percolation of water downward through surface soil is an excellent purification process. Unpleasant tastes and odors are naturally filtered. Minute quantities of minerals may be dissolved, giving well or spring water a pleasant taste. Such water is bottled and sold as mineral water. Aquifers are particular, valuable underground reservoirs that allow easy movement and pumping of water. Within an aquifer, water typically has a long residence time, perhaps centuries or millennia. Any harmful bacteria that enter an aquifer usually do not live long enough to pose a threat. Groundwater thus rarely needs treatment before drinking. Groundwater, invisible beneath our feet, is one of the Creator's priceless physical blessings for mankind and it needs to be carefully managed. We are all dependent on the precious worldwide supply of groundwater.

60. Is water dowsing reliable?

This technique for locating underground water often makes use of a forked branch from a willow tree, sometimes called a divining rod. Other dowsing devices include plastic pipe, pliers, a pendulum, whale bone, springs, bare hands, and even German sausage! A few internet and mail order companies charge extravagant prices for "guaranteed" witching rods. There is also a school in England dedicated to teaching the art of water dowsing.

A "dowser" typically walks around an area holding the divining rod and appears to feel a sharp downward pull when water is detected. Most geologists do not recognize this technique as a valid method for water location. Furthermore, science knows of no force that strongly attracts an object toward a water supply. One popular explanation is that the water is electrically *positive* and the rod *negative*, but this simply does not make physical sense. Materials such as water and rods are electrically neutral. Another doubtful idea is that dowsers are extra sensitive to tiny magnetic or electrical disturbances in the earth, somehow related to water. Some dowsers have claimed that they are distantly related to Moses, and can therefore command water from the ground as described in Numbers 20:2–13. However, Moses was led to water by the Lord, not by a forked stick. Most likely, the downward bending of a stick is caused involuntarily by the water-seeker's own hand muscles. The power of suggestion then may cause the person to believe that the rod is being pulled downward by an outside force.

Actually, of course, there is water everywhere underground. One cannot go wrong in predicting groundwater in one place or another. However, groundwater occurs at varying depths, which some dowsers are able to predict with high accuracy. Such dowsers often have had lifetime careers of seeking water by drilling wells. This background experience may give them an intuition as to the best place and depth to find water, depending on the visible lay of the land. Thus they may subconsciously bend the forked stick downward themselves, based on past drilling experience.

Dowsers sometimes search for buried pipes, oil, and even buried treasure. There seem to be no fixed rules for this activity. Some prospectors even move bent paper clips over a map in an attempt to find lost objects! It has been suggested that dowsing for water or "water witching" involves demonic forces, and therefore should be avoided by Christians. However, the divination that is condemned in scripture is the attempt to peer into future events. The search for well water seems to be an entirely different goal. Dowsing for water is of doubtful value, but it is probably not an occultic practice.

61. What is the hydrologic cycle?

King Solomon described the continuous flow of rivers 30 centuries ago,

> All the rivers run into the sea,
> Yet the sea is not full;
> To the place from which the rivers come,
> There they return again (Ecclesiastes 1:7).

Water is one of the earth's many essential interlocking cycles of matter and energy flow. Other cycles include the movement of nitrogen, carbon, oxygen, and even rocks through the environment. The transfer of water from the earth's surface to the atmosphere, then back again, is called the hydrologic or water cycle. Figure 4-5 illustrates the process with some numerical estimates. Average worldwide precipitation is about 31.5 inches (80 cm) per year. This moisture rises upward by solar evaporation of surface water and also by transpiration. Vegetation carries out this latter step by evaporation from leaves, a cooling process. A single apple tree may transfer as many as 2,000 gallons of water into the air during its growing season.

Once the water is precipitated downward as rain or snow, it begins its journey back toward sea level. It may move either as a surface stream or as groundwater. Almost all of the earth's canyons, valleys, and plains result from water erosion. On the land's surface the flow may be rapid, while underground water slowly percolates through soil and permeable rock. A rough estimate of the *average* time for a given molecule of water to move from the sea to the land and back again is 1,000

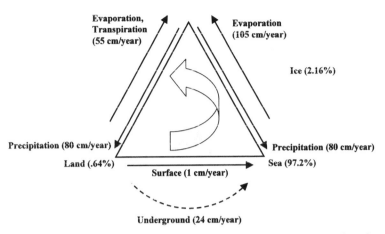

Figure 4-5. Diagram of the hydrologic cycle. Water depths are the average worldwide annual amounts in centimeters per year (cm/yr.). The distribution of the earth's total water is shown by percentages. Note that fully 2 percent of the earth's total water is frozen as ice.

years or more. Of course not all water participates in this active cycle. Fully two percent of the earth's water supply remains locked in ice with only small glacial movement. This ice covers seven percent of the earth's land area, most of it located in Antarctica. Figure 4-5 indicates that the quantity of moving underground water is at least thirty times that of surface river flow (See also Table 5-1). Rivers and lakes are impressive, but most of water's activity is underground and out of sight. This groundwater provides the earth with a remarkable purification system and reservoir. As water slowly moves downward toward the saturated water table, cleansing occurs by the breakdown and filtering of contaminants. Millions of people worldwide pump water from home wells and consume it with little concern for its purity. Unfortunately this efficient groundwater system sometimes feels the effects of abuse. Polluting of groundwater and the lowering of the water table by withdrawal could eventually lead to a water crisis of far more significance than an energy shortage.

62. How does Old Faithful work?

Old Faithful is one of more than 3,000 thermal geysers in Yellowstone National Park, Wyoming. Every 30–95 minutes, this famous geyser sends upward a fountain of hot water and steam, as high as 175 feet (53 m). Western prospectors discovered the steam jet a century ago, although it was well known to American Indians. People living in more "civilized" parts of the country did not believe the stories about steam and scalding water spouting upward from the ground. However, similar fountains also commonly occur in New Zealand and Iceland. The capital of Iceland, Reykjavik, uses water from thermal geysers and hot springs for the geothermal heating of buildings.

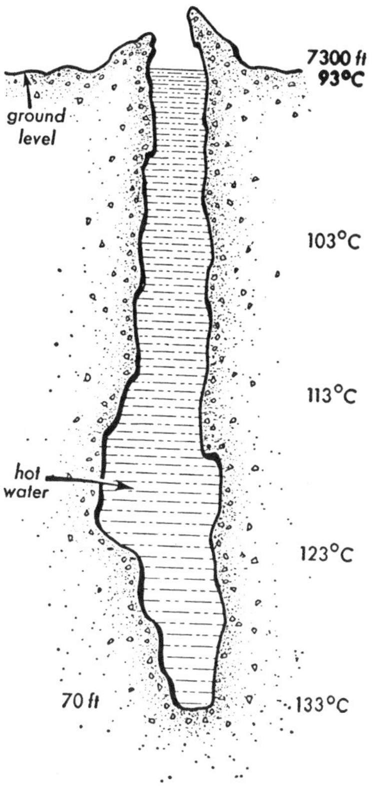

Geysers have a long, narrow underground chamber that fills with hot water (Figure 4-6). This water is then further heated by magma buried near the ground surface. At the chamber bottom, at least 70 feet (21 m) downward for Old Faithful, pressure from overlying water prevents boiling until a temperature of about 133°C (271°F) is reached. Bubbles of steam then form, which greatly increase in size as they rise upward. Near the narrow surface opening, this steam pressure expels a jet of overlying water

Figure 4-6. A diagram of the underground chamber of "Old Faithful" geyser in Yellowstone National Park, Wyoming. Parts of the channel have become quite narrow from the buildup of minerals.

with great force. The process then begins again as new ground water seeps into the underground chamber. The time period for Old Faithful has become somewhat erratic since a local earthquake occurred in 1984. This event apparently altered the flow of underground water into the chamber.

63. Why are caves cool?

Since the earth's deep interior is hot, it would seem that underground caves also should be warm. However, they usually maintain a steady cool temperature, often around 55°F (13°C). The reason for this paradox can be summed up with one word, *evaporation*. When water evaporates, heat is absorbed and cooling therefore results. Perhaps you have experienced this effect on a hot summer day after swimming. Heat calories are removed from your wet skin in the evaporation process and the result is a cool feeling. Within a cave, air currents aid the evaporation of water that continually seeps into the passages.

In some deep mines the earth's internal heat can indeed become uncomfortable. One gold mine in South Africa, 3 km deep, experiences an air temperature close to the boiling point of water. In such cases, air conditioning efforts are employed for the safety of miners.

64. What is the Lewis Overthrust?

This unusual geologic formation is found in Montana. A large region of sedimentary rock is in the wrong geologic order. In this location, older Precambrian rocks lie *above* younger Mesozoic rock layers. These rock formations are thought to differ in age by hundreds of millions of years. The overthrust region measures at least 40 miles by 350 miles, and includes the entire Glacier National Park.

The standard geologic explanation is that the older Precambrian material was thrust over the younger rock by an ancient, gradual collision between Pacific and North American crustal plates (Question 72). However, evidence is lacking for the proposed 40-mile movement of 800 trillion tons of Pre-

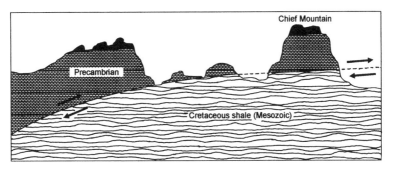

Figure 4-7. A portion of the Lewis Overthrust in Montana. Chief Mountain is a large structure of solid rock weighing millions of tons (Plummer et. al, 2003, p. 372).

cambrian rock directly over the top of younger rock. Figure 4-7 shows one portion of the "overthrust" including Chief Mountain. There is little ground-up rock material between the layers where massive grinding surely would have occurred. Also, the top rock shows very little tilting or dip, only about 3 degrees. Because of this data, some geologists have proposed that the Lewis Overthrust has been completely misinterpreted. Instead of large-scale movement, the sedimentary layers may have formed in place just as we find them, perhaps during the Genesis Flood. This view challenges the validity of the assumed order of the uniformitarian geologic column.

The Lewis Overthrust does not stand alone as an out-of-sequence structure. Similar reversals occur in other mountain ranges around the world, including the Jura Mountains of Europe. The question is unsettled regarding the origin of these overthrusts. Even if the formations are overthrusts, the billion-year age interpretation is unnecessary. These "rock puzzles" shows how little we really know about the major details of the earth's crustal features.

65. What is Specimen Ridge?

This name is given to a particular cliff in the Fossil Forest region of Yellowstone National Park. The 1200 foot-high ridge exposes 27 distinct layers of buried volcanic sediments. These

Figure 4-8. A cross-section of Specimen Ridge in Yellowstone National Park (Dorf, 1964). Note the many layers of fossil tree trunks and volcanic sediments.

layers also contain many petrified tree trunks. Figure 4-8 is a cross-section of Specimen Ridge drawn by geologist William H. Holmes in 1878. The standard explanation is that each layer represents an entire forest that slowly grew to maturity, then suddenly was destroyed and buried by volcanic mud flows (Dorf, 1964). Following petrification and erosion, an entire new forest then grew upon the base of the former. To repeat this process 27 times would require at least 40–60 thousand years. Therefore Specimen Ridge has been offered by critics as a direct contradiction to the young earth view of history.

Specimen Ridge involves additional data that is often neglected. For example, complete root systems are not found for the petrified trees, but only small "root balls." Evidence of accumulated bark and limbs is also missing. There are compressed layers of organic materials but no soils. And some of the petrified tree trunks closely overlap each other in the strata. Dendrochronology studies indicate that many of the vertically separated trees seem to have lived and died at nearly the same time. Also, the mineral content is very similar for all the multiple tree layers, as if they were petrified simultaneously.

From this data, an alternate explanation is that the 27 layers of tree stumps were rapidly deposited upon one another at the time of the Genesis Flood (Austin, 1986). "Floating forests" in the form of log mats probably were plentiful upon the floodwaters until they became waterlogged and sank. The Specimen Ridge region, at a lower elevation and submerged at that time, thus became a collection site for uprooted tree trunks that had been stripped of their roots and limbs. A somewhat similar accumulation was observed in Spirit Lake following the Mount St. Helen's eruption (Question 49). Specimen Ridge may thus be a monument to catastrophe instead of a monument to time.

66. How did Niagara Falls form?

The Niagara River is only 35 miles long (56 km) and connects Lake Erie with Lake Ontario. It also forms the boundary between Canada and New York. The river formed relatively recently, at the end of the Ice Age. Geologist Charles Lyell visited the Falls in 1841 and declared them to be 35,000 years old (Pierce, 2000). Secular geology currently places their formation at 10,000-30,000 years ago. Most creationists would

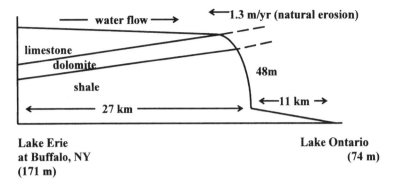

Figure 4-9. A side view of the Niagara River and Falls. The tilt of the dolomite layer is about 7 meters per kilometer. In parentheses are the elevations of the Great Lakes Erie and Ontario.

shorten this time considerably. Probably meltwater at the end of the Ice Age caused Lake Erie to overflow and cut through the Niagara Gorge, forming the famous Falls.

Niagara Falls drops about 158 feet (48 m). Each second, 700,000 gallons of water cascade into the Niagara Gorge below. At the top edge of the Falls is a tilted layer of dolomite, a mineral composed of calcium magnesium carbonate (Figure 4-9). It is this resistant rock that maintains the vertical cliff. As the falling water gradually undercuts weaker shale rock beneath the cliff, the dolomite lip crumbles and the Falls migrate upstream. If left unchecked, this erosion causes the Falls to retreat upstream an average of 1.3 meters/year. After slow migration about 5 miles upstream, the Falls would eventually disappear and become whitewater rapids. This change would take place within 7,000 years assuming a constant river flow. However, further erosion of Niagara Falls is largely prevented by engineers for the sake of tourism and also for electrical power generation. They are able to divert water through large tunnels and also reinforce the rocks at the edge of the Falls. This majestic waterfall demonstrates the sound and power of unleashed water. It remains one of the most popular tourist sites in North America.

67. What are the La Brea tar pits?

Today this unusual area is surrounded by the city of Los Angeles and is preserved as a park and museum. There are acre-size pools of black tar, also called pitch, asphalt, or bitumen. The material consists of oily hydrocarbons that may be either organic or inorganic in origin. This California location is not unique. Similar sources of tar have long been known around the Dead Sea, in the Ukraine, and also in modern Iraq. Elsewhere, there is the one-mile wide Pitch Lake on the island of Trinidad in the West Indies. This tar is used to pave roads in Trinidad. Workers have drilled 300 feet into the lake and found no bottom to the black tar.

Bitumen seepages work their way upward to the earth's surface from deep reservoirs. The ark of Noah was caulked with such pitch (Gen. 6:14), as well as the basket that hid the infant Moses (Ex. 2:3). Tar likewise was used for mortar between bricks in the Tower of Babel (Gen. 11:3). Genesis 14:10 also describes Canaanite soldiers falling into tar pits near the cities of Sodom and Gomorrah.

California's La Brea tar pits are a cemetery for tens of thousands of animals that became mired in the gooey tar. These include saber-toothed tigers, llamas, dire wolves, camels, horses, mastodons, mammoths, giant ground sloths, and birds. One creationist view is that the animals were washed into the tar seeps during the Flood. Another traditional view is that large animals occasionally became trapped in the pitch. This attracted predators which likewise became ensnared in the tar. Geologists categorize the La Brea animals as *Pleistocene* which dates them at about 10–40 thousand years ago. Most young-earth scientists would place the period of animal entrapment in postFlood times, just a few thousand years ago. Evidence for this more recent view includes the skeleton of an American Indian that was found in 1914 beneath the bones of an extinct vulture in La Brea's black ooze. The female appears to be the victim of a severe blow to the head. Native Americans generally are thought to have inhabited the Southwest U.S. only during the last few thousand years.

68. What causes earthquakes?

The earth shakes when energy in the form of motion is suddenly released underground. One of the most common places this occurs is along the edges of the continental plate boundaries around the rim of the Pacific Ocean. See Question 72 for a description of the earth's crustal plates. If one plots on a map the locations of earthquake epicenters, there is a close correlation with plate margins (Figure 4-10). The Pacific boundary also is called the *ring of fire* because of its association with volcanoes as well as earthquakes. Fault lines are associated with the areas where two plates meet, and therefore with earthquake regions. Stress builds up along these plate margins, then is suddenly released by crustal movement. When earthquakes occur they result in vibrations that ripple through the earth, shaking the land and buildings above. Every day there are thousands of small earthquake tremors around the world.

It is sometimes suggested that California will eventually "slide" into the Pacific Ocean and disappear. Actually, how-

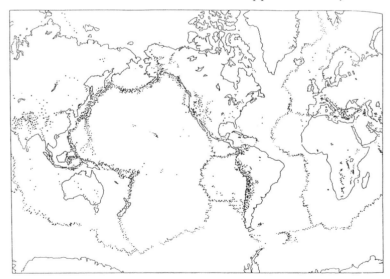

Figure 4-10. A world map showing the locations of earthquake epicenters over a ten year period. Earthquakes tend to occur along crustal plate boundaries.

ever, the Pacific Plate and western California coast are tending to move north, while the North America Plate moves south (Figure 4-11). The San Andreas fault line which separates the plates in this region is called a *strike-slip* fault. Given unlimited time, California's coastal cities including Los Angeles and San Francisco would gradually move far northward rather than into the sea. The majority of U.S. earthquakes actually do not take place in California. The percentage of total U.S. earthquakes, mainly slight tremors are:

Figure 4-11. California and the San Andreas fault zone (dotted line). The arrows show the relative, opposite movements of the Pacific and North American plates on the west and east sides of the San Andreas fault.

Hawaii, 35%; California, 25%; Alaska, 10%; and elsewhere, 30%.

69. Can earthquakes be predicted?

Success in earthquake prediction has been very limited. Unexpected earthquake tragedies continue to occur across the earth. One current effort at prediction involves the study of unusual animal behavior. A large variety of creatures have shown restlessness or disorientation, hours or days before an earthquake strikes. Included are dogs, pigs, cattle, rats, and snakes. Burrowing animals have been seen to leave their tunnels in the hours before an earthquake. Apparently these creatures can sense impending danger, perhaps feeling tiny precursor ground movements.

A second effort at quake prediction involves the monitoring of well water. In the days or weeks before an earthquake occurs, microscopic cracks may appear in underground rocks due to the intense buildup of stress. This causes a slight expansion or rise in the above land surface, as is currently happening around Palmdale, California. The uplift has amounted to several inches in recent years. The developing rock fissures also allow an increased movement of ground water. Radon, a natural radioactive gas found underground, then may be carried rapidly into well water. An increase in detected radon, dissolved in the well water, may indicate an imminent earthquake. Many wells in western states are monitored for telltale changes in radon context.

70. Which U.S. State has experienced the most severe earthquake?

This "honor" goes to the state of Missouri. Pioneer diaries describe at least three very severe earthquakes that shook the lower Midwest two centuries ago, during 1811–1812. The events were of magnitude 8 or greater on a 1–10 scale. They were centered on the "Bootheel" region of Missouri near New Madrid (Ma' drid). During each earthquake the ground continued to churn for weeks, toppling log cabins. The ground also rose upward as much as 20 feet, forcing the nearby Mississippi River to flow northward temporarily. Portions of Illinois and Wisconsin to the North were flooded as a result. Seven hundred miles away, East Coast church bells were caused to sway and ring. The following is a brief description from a pioneer diary, as published by modern author Mary Dohan in a book titled *Mr. Roosevelt's Steamboat* (Dohan, 1981).

People woke to an "awful darkness" and a sulphurous, choking mist. They heard the rumble of thunder deep in the earth and the crash of chimneys. Fissures opened beneath people's feet and from yawning holes spouted jets of warm water, sand, and coal that flew as high as the tops of trees. In the morning they found on the ground the massive bones of dinosaurs that had been long buried. Some people died of fright, others by drowning. There was sound like artillery fire-hissing discharges exploding from funnellike holes in the earth. A mountain was ripped apart at Knoxville, Tennessee, with a terrible noise and flashes of fire.

Four miles beneath Missouri's ground surface there has been found a zone of fault lines which triggered the historic earthquake. Earthquakes usually repeat themselves. Therefore, when stresses have sufficiently built up, a large earthquake may again shake the Midwestern states. Whether the frequency of occurrence is 200 years so that another earthquake is imminent, or perhaps 500 years, is unknown.

71. Is the number of earthquakes increasing?

Catastrophes often turn our minds toward end time prophecies. Wars, volcanoes, famine, disease, severe storms, and earthquakes—all these events cause us to consider the future of mankind. It is tempting to watch for particular signs of the end of this present age. In particular, earthquakes long have been studied for a possible increasing trend in occurrence. Figure 4-12 shows the number of recorded earthquake fatalities during the past 1500 years. Numbers indeed have increased in recent years, due mainly to larger populations living in cities. However, the figure also shows that many deaths have occurred in previous centuries. In counting actual earthquakes, there are found to be fewer earthquakes in

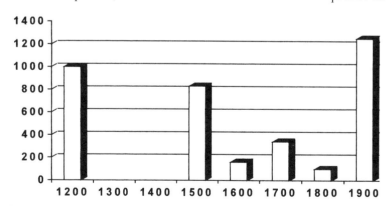

Figure 4-12. The bar graph estimates the number of earthquake-related fatalities (in thousands) over the centuries, worldwide, as tabulated in several Almanacs.

the last 50 years than in the previous half-century (Austin and Strauss, 1999).

The creation view of history suggests that more earthquakes occurred in the past than the present. Much of the energy currently released during earthquake events probably was stored within the earth during the year of Noah's Flood. At that time the earth's entire crust was deformed by massive fissures, sediment deposition, erosion, and mountain building processes. In the few thousand years since the flood occurred, the earth's surface has continued to adjust itself and seek equilibrium. This results in occasional earthquakes that still continue today.

Scripture cautions against attempts to exactly date the end of the world:

> You will hear of wars and rumors of wars,
> See that you are not troubled;
> For all these things must come to pass, but the end is not yet.
> For nation will rise against nation, and kingdom against kingdom.
> And there will be famines, pestilences, and earthquakes in various places.
> All these are the beginning of sorrows.
>
> Matthew 24: 6–8

Also, Mark 13:32 reminds us that no one except the Father knows the exact time of the final events which accompany our Lord's return to earth. Science data is very useful but it cannot pinpoint the end of this age.

72. Do the continents move?

This topic has dominated geology for several decades. Acceptance of large-scale continental drift is by no means unanimous. For a contrary view, see for example (Reed, 2000). However, this discussion will consider the majority view. One item of data supporting the movement of the earth's continents is the apparent fit of the coastlines (actually the continental shelves) of separate continents, somewhat like pieces of a giant jigsaw puzzle (Figure 4-10). This fit was described long ago by Francis Bacon (1561–1626), and more recently by Alfred Wegener (1880–1930). The impression is that continents like South America and Africa, or North America and Europe, were once combined into a single, large landmass. This original supercontinent is called *Pangaea*, meaning "one land." It may be indicated in Genesis 1:9–10, when the earth's water is gathered into the seas. This may imply a single landmass with surrounding seas. On a smaller scale the original picture may have been similar to Australia today. This country is surrounded by the Tasman, Coral, Arafura, and Timor Seas; and also the Indian and Pacific Oceans.

The continents and oceans are actually part of the earth's crust, the solidified, uppermost layer of our planet. This crust is divided into seven major and several minor "plates" which occasionally jostle against each other. They are outlined in Figure 4-10. The plates lie above the earth's mantle, a deeper, dense region of the earth's interior. Some of the plates appear to be growing in regions called ocean *ridges*, seams in the crust where new material is extruded upward from within the earth. At other boundaries the plate edges dip back into the mantle and remelt in deep ocean *trenches* (Figure 4-13; Oard, 2001). The motion of these plates is thought to be driven by heat convection from below, somewhat like a pot of boiling stew. The location of many earthquake epicenters and volcanoes matches with the colliding plate edges. As the plates grind against each other in slow motion, stresses build up, and sudden ground movement periodically occurs. This overall process of crustal movement is called *plate tectonics*.

One of the largest features on earth is an ocean ridge that winds completely around the earth, somewhat like the seam on a baseball. It extends from the Arctic region down the center of the Atlantic Ocean. It then branches across the Indian and South Pacific Oceans, ending in the Gulf of California. This remarkable ridge is about 40,000 miles (65,000 km) long and 840 miles (1400 km) wide. Some of its adjacent mountain peaks extend more than a mile above the seafloor.

Many geologists propose that Pangaea split up during the Jurassic period, about 200 million years ago. They also suggest

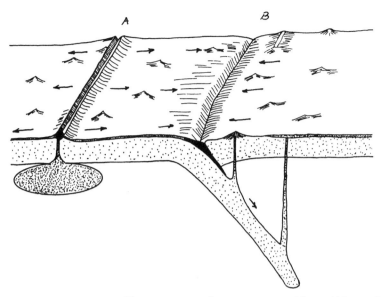

Figure 4-13. An illustration of an ocean ridge (A) and trench (B), both located on the seafloor. These features gradually recycle the earth's crust. Arrows show the ground movement of the crust.

that there may have been multiple earlier supercontinents and breakups. As expected, creationists have a different viewpoint. For example, present day continental drift or seafloor spreading probably occurs at a much slower rate than in the past. North America and Europe are currently separating at about two inches per year, approximately the rate of fingernail growth. This slow motion is measured by laser survey methods using satellites. Many creationists believe that continental drift occurred rapidly during the Genesis Flood, a time of worldwide catastrophic change. Genesis 7:11 declares that the "foundations of the deep" split open as a source of the floodwaters. Also, at the conclusion of the Flood, the mountains rose up and the valleys sank down according to Psalm 104:6–9 (Question 53). These references may imply a splitting of the earth's crust into separate plates with subsequent lateral motion. *Second*, some have suggested that continental drift may also have been a part of the Tower of Babel story in

Genesis 11. A contemporary of the Babel story was Peleg, in whose day "the earth was divided" (Genesis 10:25). However, this reference is more likely the division of languages than a physical land separation.

In summary, a creationist evaluation of continental drift calls for catastrophic change in the past and a gradual, slowing approach to equilibrium still continuing today. One creationist prediction might be that continental drift will eventually cease entirely in the distant future. This view contrasts sharply with the standard geology view that continental drift always has occurred slowly and continually over billions of years. Hopefully, future study and data collection will resolve this issue.

73. How do mountains form?

The process of mountain formation is called *orogenesis*. Enormous forces are involved in the movement of earth material. Three categories will be mentioned here. *First*, volcanism is the only mountain formation activity observed directly. Volcanoes may slowly build a conical mountain of ash, or may explosively remove a mountaintop, as with the Mount St. Helens eruption in 1980. *Second*, many mountain ranges are composed of folded, crumpled sedimentary rock strata. Examples include the Alps, Andes, and Appalachian mountain belts. Many such folded formations may result from the Flood event as the fountains of the deep were opened. There is evidence of great compressional and tensional forces between portions of the earth's crust worldwide, forming these mountains (Oard, 2002). *Third*, many mountain ranges show faulted, deformed blocks of rock, as if rock layers were displaced by upward thrusting. This requires great vertical forces from within the earth. The Sierra Nevada (California), Tetons (Wyoming), and portions of the Rocky Mountain range are fault-block mountains.

Mountains are supported by an increased crustal thickness of material beneath them. The mountains float on the mantle with much of their supporting foundation out of sight below, somewhat like great battleships at sea. The earth's crust averages 15–75 km (9–47 miles) in thickness, and is thickest beneath mountains. This buoyant "floating" of mountains on the mantle is called *isostasy*.

74. Is the Earth hollow?

There is no physical evidence for this unusual idea although it has been proposed by individuals in the distant and recent past. Dante's *Divine Comedy*, written seven centuries ago, describes a journey downward through 24 levels of Hell to the center of the earth. In 1692, astronomer Edmund Halley suggested that three additional concentric, hollow planets existed inside the earth. Mathematicians Leonard Euler and John Leslie proposed that there might be additional suns within the earth. Jules Verne described such a hollow earth is his 1872 science fiction book, *A Journey to the Center of the Earth*. Jules Verne's subterranean world was filled with prehistoric creatures.

Another bizarre view is that a race of people actually lives on the inside surface of a hollow earth, with another sun at the center. The poles are said to be openings into this internal world. Adherents of this offbeat idea see hidden meaning in the words of Admiral Richard Byrd, the first man to fly over the North Pole in 1947, "I'd like to see that land beyond the North Pole. That area is the center of the great unknown." Actually, Byrd was simply describing the desolate expanse of the Arctic region, not some mysterious opening into a hollow earth. There are internet sites today that continue to defend a hollow earth.

It must be admitted that we cannot explore the deep interior of the earth (Question 75). Could there actually be a cavity within the lower depths, perhaps even the location of a literal hell? From a physical basis, the great internal pressures from overlying rock would seem to rule out this possibility. However, current uncertainty about the earth's interior calls for caution in drawing any such conclusion. It is of interest that the book of Revelation seven times refers to a "bottomless pit" descending into the earth, the abode of the devil (Rev. 9: 1,2,11; 11:7; 17:8; 20:1,3).

75. How deep have geologists drilled into the earth?

During the 1960s there was an attempt by the U.S. to drill entirely through the earth's crust and obtain samples from the mantle beneath. Oceanic crust was chosen since it is thinner than continental crust (Question 73). This deep drilling effort was called *Project Mohole* and was located under the Pacific Ocean off Mexico's coast. The project was eventually abandoned after several miles depth because of the growing expense and technical difficulties. Likewise, a drill hole in Oklahoma was stopped at 6 miles (9.7 km) depth when it encountered molten sulfur. At such depths, both heat and pressure make drilling very difficult. One is reminded of Jeremiah 31:37,

> If heaven above can be measured,
> and the foundations of the earth searched out beneath,
> I will cast off all the seed of Israel
> for all that they have done, says the Lord.

True to the verse, we cannot search out the inner depths of the earth, nor can we enter deep space. Therefore God's promises are secure.

Russia currently holds the depth record with an Arctic hole drilled 7.5 miles (12 kilometers) deep. In this lower portion of earth's crust the researchers were surprised to find liquid water, traces of hydrogen and methane gases, and also copper-nickel ore. For a time in the 1980s there was a popular story that the Soviets had heard human groans from their deep hole, accompanied by sulfur fumes, as if they had penetrated into hell itself! This story is a complete hoax, one of many "urban legends" that continue to circulate (Buhler, 1990). Scripture is clear regarding the reality of hell, and perhaps it is located deep within the earth. However, the Russian drilling story trivializes the seriousness of the subject. God is not in the business of revealing the actual location of either heaven or hell to skeptics.

76. What are some of the earth's landmarks made of?

The following alphabetical lists describe representative natural and cultural (manmade) landmarks.

Natural landmarks

Ayers Rock (*Uluru*) in central Australia consists of reddish arkose sandstone. It is the world's largest monolith, or single rock structure.

The *Badlands* of South Dakota are weathered shale formations located in a very dry region. Fossils of turtles are found, indicating a moist climate in the distant past.

The *Bonneville Salt Flats* in Utah are evaporite deposits including halite, gypsum, and borax. Much of this mineral material has washed in from surrounding mountains.

The *Cliffs of Dover* rise hundreds of feet above the Strait of Dover on southeast England's coast. They consist of chalk, a variety of fossil limestone.

Devil's Tower, in Wyoming is an igneous dike, the remnant of a volcanic mountain exposed by erosion. The rock tower stands 865 feet (263 meters) high and has a flat top.

El Capitan and *Half Dome* in Yosemite National Park are immense granite structures. This is also true of Colorado's *Pikes Peak* and New Hampshire's *White Mountains*.

The *Grand Canyon* of Arizona exposes multiple sedimentary layers of shale, limestone, and sandstone. At the bottom is metamorphic rock with igneous intrusions.

Australia's *Great Barrier Reef* consists of a vast coral colony made of the mineral calcium carbonate, $CaCO_3$. This reef, 1260 miles (2100 km) long, supports a great diversity of sea life.

Israel's historic fortress plateau called *Masada* is made of limestone, common the Middle East.

Mount Everst (29,035 feet, 8850 m) on the frontier of Nepal and Tibet has a yellow band of marine limestone near its summit. Beneath this layer is dark metamorphic gneiss.

The *Rock of Gibraltar* is a massive block of gray limestone. It stands nearly 1400 feet (425 m) high and is located on the south-central coast of Spain, at the entrance to the Mediterranean Sea from the Atlantic Ocean.

Atlanta Georgia's *Stone Mountain* is a large outcrop of granite. It rises 780 feet (238 m) above the surrounding area.

Ship Rock in New Mexico is a volcanic *rock* 1700 feet (518 m) high. It is the remnant of an earlier volcanic mountain.

Cultural landmarks:

The ancient temple at *Angor Wat*, Cambodia, is made of bricks of a red soil called laterite.

Common *arrowhead* materials in North America were chert quartz (also called flint) and obsidian.

Michelangelo's *David* sculpture, completed during 1501–1504, is carved from white marble.

The *Empire State Building* is sided with Indiana limestone and East Coast granite.

The *Leaning Tower of Pisa* is made of white marble.

The *Lincoln Memorial* in Washington D.C. is made of white marble from Colorado and Alabama.

India's *Taj Mahal* is covered with inlaid marble.

The *Mesa Verde* cliff dwellings of Arizona lie within a sandstone and shale formation.

The *Mount Rushmore* presidential figures are carved in a granite cliff in the Black Hills of South Dakota.

Many ancient Egyptian *obelisks* are variously made of granite, basalt, and quartzite.

The *Parthenon* of Athens, Greece is made of limestone.

The *pyramids* have an exterior surface of limestone blocks. The Great Pyramid of Khufu at Giza contains more than one million blocks.

The *Roman Coliseum, St. Peter's Cathedral* in Rome, and New York's *Pennsylvania Railroad Station* are all made of the mineral *travertine* quarried near Rome, Italy.

The *Rosetta Stone* inscriptions are carved on a tablet of black basalt.

The base of the *Statue of Liberty* is Connecticut granite.

The *walls* of the Old City of Jerusalem consist of great blocks of limestone.

77. Is the earth either shrinking or expanding?

These unconventional ideas were popular a century ago. The idea of a shrinking earth is a historical attempt to explain the earth's rugged surface features. Leading geologists such as James Dana (1813 – 1895) once favored this proposal, as still do a few modern geologists. Consider an apple or an orange that is allowed to dry out and shrivel. The resulting folds and creases on its skin somewhat resemble miniature versions of the earth's mountain ranges. As the apple (or the earth) further shrinks, the topography slowly changes. This is an interesting analogy, but historical measurements do not show any such reduction in the earth's radius. Also, there is no known physical mechanism that would lead to a decreasing size for the earth.

An opposite idea to earth contraction is a gradually expanding world. Such movement could explain the separation and drift of continents as a result of an increasing surface area on the earth. As with earth shrinkage, however, there is a lack of supporting data or a mechanism for such a fundamental change in the size of our planet.

Chapter Five
The Seas

78. What are some theories of ocean origin?

There is no scientific consensus on the origin of ocean waters. One popular theory suggests that volcanoes long ago released all of the earth's surface water from internal reservoirs. Others believe that comets from space delivered the ocean waters to earth. Neither idea has strong supporting evidence. In both theories, the water itself somehow originated in the early solar system in an unknown way.

Genesis 1:2 states that abundant water covered the earth at the time of its supernatural creation, and this water has been present ever since. It occurs on the earth in all three of its physical states: as solid ice, as a liquid, and as vapor or humidity. A water molecule itself is stable up to a temperature of 2600°C (4712°F), hotter even than rock magma. Therefore the earth's water is a permanent feature, a gift from the Creator.

79. How much total water is in the oceans?

The earth looks like a blue oasis in space since it is about 71 percent covered with seas. Only traces of water have been found elsewhere in the solar system. Our vast oceans of water average over two miles deep. And in the Mariana Trench of the western Pacific Ocean near Guam, the water depth reaches nearly seven miles. A large stone thrown overboard at this location would sink for nearly two hours before hitting bottom! Table 5-1 shows the distribution of the earth's water. If divided equally among the world's population, there would be nearly 70 billion gallons of water for every single person. That much water would fill an entire lake measuring one mile across. In spite of this, water shortages still occur because of the lack of available fresh, clean water in many locations.

Table 5-1 shows that most of the world's fresh water is in the form of ice, almost all of it located in Antarctica (See also Fig-

Table 5-1. The estimated distribution of the earth's total water reserves. The published percentages vary slightly. The four minor categories after the oceans are all fresh water. The movement of surface and underground water is indicated in Figure 4-5.

Water Location	Percent of earth's total water
Oceans	97.2
Ice	2.16
Underground	.62
Surface (lakes, rivers)	.02
Atmosphere	Trace

ure 4-5). There has been some thought of towing southern icebergs to distant parts of the world where fresh water is in short supply. If this fresh water then was recovered, it could supply large cities for hundreds of years. The transport of such large icebergs, if economically and technologically possible, could drastically change regional climates.

Precipitation pours down on the earth in the amount of 1.5 trillion tons each day. This movement of water throughout the hydrologic cycle is the most important agent in shaping the earth's surface. Canyons, valleys, rolling hills, and plains are all formed by moving water. The weathering or breaking down of rocks into soil is also accomplished by water in two specific ways. *Chemically*, water causes minerals to dissolve; *mechanically*, expansion and contraction due to temperature changes eventually fracture rocks into smaller pieces.

As everyone knows, water is essential to all life on earth. Medical science has found that humans can survive for several weeks without food, but only for a few days without water. This resource is just one of God's multiple, precious gifts to our planet.

80. What causes a tsunami?

Tsunami is a Japanese word meaning an overflowing wave. These destructive waves are caused by submarine earthquakes rather than lunar tides. Also called seismic waves, they result when an earthquake raises a portion of the seafloor, disturbing the water above. The resulting waves spread outward like ripples on a pond, gaining greatly in height near shallow shorelines. The highest such tsunami known struck England's northern Shetland Islands several millennia ago. There is physical evidence remaining on the mountainsides that the giant wave was 1,180 feet high (360 m) and moved at 110 miles per hour (177 km/hr). On a smaller scale, tsunamis can also occur on inland lakes. There is historical evidence for mountain landslides of debris into California's Lake Tahoe, causing waves 30 feet high.

A great tsunami struck the Ryukyu chain of Japanese islands in 1771. This surge picked up an 800-ton block of coral from the sea bottom and carried it more than 1.3 miles inland. In 1868, a Hawaiian surfer named Holua actually rode a tsunami! He was caught in the 50-foot wave as it approached Minole, Hawaii, and successfully rode it shoreward to save his life. Some modern tsunamis have speeds as great as 600 miles per hour (965 km/hr). Another type of immense "rogue" waves occurs in the open ocean when several smaller sea waves converge by chance and add together. Such waves may tower over ships and destroy them suddenly (Flatow, 1989). These ocean disturbances reveal the great energy of the sea and its destructive power when unleashed.

81. Has the Mediterranean Sea dried up in the past?

The Mediterranean Sea is connected to the Atlantic Ocean at the Strait of Gibraltar (Figure 5-1). If this entry were closed off, the entire sea could evaporate to dryness in about 1,000 years. Geologists have proposed that continental drift indeed isolated the Mediterranean Sea in this way about six million years ago. Evidence includes 2-km-thick (1.24 mi) evaporite beds on the current seafloor. Also, rivers flowing into the Mediterranean Sea have deep submarine canyons near their mouths, now submerged offshore. It is thought that these valleys were carved when the Mediterranean Sea was at a much lower level.

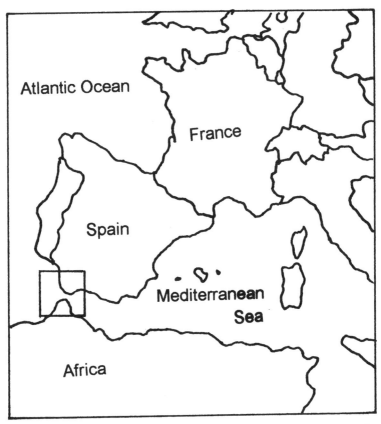

Figure 5-1. A map of the Mediterranean or Great Sea. The Strait of Gibraltar is at the west end of the Sea, in the small box.

Some geologists propose that evaporation and refilling of the Mediterranean has occurred many times over as land masses jostled back and forth, opening and closing the Gibraltar strait. Others reject the entire idea, explaining that the evaporite beds may form by precipitation within the deep, water-filled sea basin. Such a *hydrothermal* origin of evaporites could have occurred during the Flood when increased volcanic and magmatic activity heated the floodwaters. When mixed with cooler water, evaporite precipitation then could result. Creationist geology could possibly allow multiple cycles of drying and refilling of the Mediterranean Sea basin, depending on unknown rates of evaporation in the past. If one or more such events has indeed occurred, the Strait of Gibraltar would have provided dynamic views. The floor of the Mediterranean lies 3 km (1.86 mi) below sea level. If ocean water broke through the Strait into a dry Mediterranean seabed, it might have resulted in a waterfall thousands of times greater than Niagara.

82. What are turbidity currents?

On November 18, 1929, transatlantic communication was suddenly interrupted. The problem began with an earthquake off the coast of Newfoundland. This quake caused a vast movement of sediment down the continental slope and across the sea floor. Moving at 50 miles per hour (80 km/hr), this underwater *turbidity current* snapped a dozen thick metal cables lying on the ocean floor, one after the other, over a distance of 400 miles (600 km). Sections of heavy marine cable 60 miles long (100km) were broken loose and carried completely away by the surging current. Until this time, many geologists doubted the existence of such forceful underwater landslides. It is now known that turbidity currents can be triggered by earthquakes, storms, and sediment-laden rivers. Such high-speed currents of sediment probably were present during the Flood, reshaping the earth's surface.

83. What geologic features are on the sea bottom?

The earth is about 71 percent covered with seawater. Hidden below on the ocean floor is a great variety of interesting features. Directly offshore from land are the *continental shelves*, the submerged edges of the continents. Much of this land may have been exposed during the Ice Age when sea levels were lower. These shallow shelves today are home to a great variety of sea life. Beyond the shelves lies the *continental slope*. This is a relatively steep drop-off to the great ocean depths beyond. Many of these slopes are cut by great *submarine canyons* that resemble drowned river valleys. The large ravines either were formed by rivers when exposed as dry land, or else they result from underwater current erosion. Across the ocean floor appear thousands of dormant *submarine volcanoes*. Many are flat-topped due to erosion, and are called *seamounts*. The area of the western Pacific basin alone has an estimated 10,000 sub-merged seamounts. Some of the oceanic volcanic peaks rise above sea level to form islands. The Hawaiian Islands actually are exposed mountain peaks. Another nameless peak lies between Samoa and New Zealand. It is 28,500 feet high (8687 m), similar in size to Mt. Everest, yet this peak remains 1,200 feet (366 m) beneath the ocean surface.

The ocean floor has many mountain ranges, some associated with *ridges*. Ridges are crustal cracks or faults where magma is moving upward. The Mid-Atlantic Ridge (Question 72) is a source of undersea volcanoes, hot springs, and earthquakes. The ocean ridges are complemented by *trenches*; deep crevices where crustal material is sinking downward into the earth's mantle (Figure 4-13). This rock is melted, perhaps later to again move upward as recycled crust. Many of the ocean floor features can be explained by the Flood events: continental breakup, widespread volcanism, and the subsequent appearance of ridges and trenches.

84. Are there "paths" in the sea?

There are many paths through the seas, as described in Psalm 8:8,

> You have made [man] to have dominion over…
> The birds of the air, and the fish of the sea
> That pass through the paths of the seas…

One set of pathways is the ocean currents that circulate vast amounts of water worldwide. The Gulf Stream is such a current, carrying a volume of water equal to 1,000 Mississippi Rivers. It may be described as a giant moving river within the ocean itself. The Gulf Stream circles the North Atlantic basin, delivering an immense quantity of heat from the equator to Western Europe and the Arctic. Norway is warmed by these Gulf waters to a temperature which is 28°C (50.4°F) higher than the average for its northern latitude.

An early scientist who studied the pattern of ocean currents was Matthew Maury (1806–1873). He is sometimes called the "Father of Oceanography" and also the "Pathfinder of the Seas." This latter title is inscribed on his tombstone at the U.S. Naval Academy in Annapolis, Maryland. Here is a quote from his 1855 book, *Physical Geography of the Sea*, concerning the Gulf Stream:

> There is a river in the ocean: in the severest draught it never fails, and in the mightiest floods it never overflows: its banks and bottom are of cold water, while its current is of warm; the Gulf of Mexico is its fountain, and its mouth is the Arctic Seas.

This was the first textbook on oceanography. Matthew Maury was injured in an 1839 stagecoach accident in Ohio that ended his naval career. Forced to remain ashore, he began to analyze the logs of sailing ships. In this way Maury discovered the patterns of ocean currents. He discovered that there were vast ocean channels similar to trails across the land. All his life Maury maintained a strong Christian testimony. He explained that he was motivated in his research by Psalm 8:8 which describes the "paths of the seas."

Another set of paths form the migratory routes of whales and other sea creatures. Birds such as Arctic Terns migrate across the oceans using island landmarks and also surface currents to tell direction. Perhaps David was aware of the migration habits of these creatures in his Psalm 8:8 reference to the paths of the seas.

85. What are the "springs of the sea?"

Springs occur when underground water is forced to the earth's surface by pressure. Long ago, the Lord explained to Job that large bodies of water were fed by underwater "springs of the sea,"

> Have you entered the springs of the sea?
> Or have you walked in search of the depths? Job 38:16

This reference is one of many accurate, *anticipatory* scientific insights from Scripture.

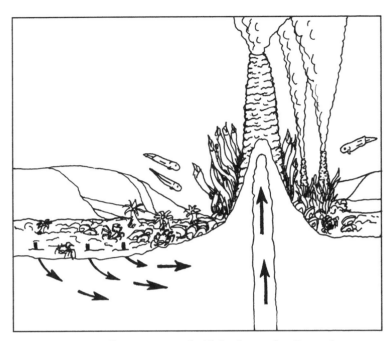

Figure 5-2. An illustration of a "black smoker" on the ocean floor. Notice the living creatures gathered around the vent.

In recent decades, springs of up-welling water have been located in the depths of the oceans. The first detailed look at these hydrothermal vents or sea springs occurred in 1977. At this time National Geographic explorers descended into the ocean near the Galapagos Islands using the small submersible *Alvin*. They were amazed to find abundant sea life near the springs in spite of the great water pressure and total darkness. Hot water emitted from the sea floor supplies the necessary energy for creatures such as fish, shrimp, tubeworms, sea urchins, white crabs, clams, and microbes. Some of the vents are called "black smokers" since they spew out clouds of 350°C (660°F) water laden with dark sulfides, iron, and other minerals. The mineral deposits form chimneys, mounds, and spires. A calcium carbonate chimney found east of Bermuda in the Mid-Atlantic Ocean is 18 stories tall (60 m).

Some scientists have suggested that in the early oceans, heat from deep sea vents might have helped produce the first living organisms on earth from raw chemicals. There has long been the popular evolutionary view that life somehow began in the sea. However, amino acids, the elementary building blocks of life, would be destroyed within seconds by the intense heat of the superheated ocean springs. In general, complex molecules are quickly broken apart or *pyrolyzed* by high temperatures. The undersea animals observed today must maneuver carefully around the jets of hot water to avoid being cooked! There is a second problem with the idea that life was first incubated near deep sea thermal vents. Most of these vents appear to be short-lived, lasting only several years before they are completely plugged up by minerals. Meanwhile, unlimited time and ideal, steady conditions are essential parts of most origin of life theories.

The vast majority of undersea springs remain unexplored and unseen. Only the Lord is able to oversee and micromanage the complex details of his magnificent creation, including the springs of the sea.

86. What happens to oil spills?

Oil spills in the ocean have received wide publicity. These include the Torrey Canyon tanker spill off England's coast (1967), several Santa Barbara oil platform "blowouts," and the *Exxon Valdez* tanker collision in Prince William Sound, Alaska (1989). This particular accident spilled 11 million gallons of crude oil into the sea. Pictures of blackened beaches and struggling sea birds are all too common.

Crude oil consists of hundreds of chemicals, and the full extent of its detrimental effects on sea life is not known. Efforts to clean up oil spills include the dispersal of straw and detergents which emulsify, dissolve, or sink the escaped oil. Certain bacteria can also break down oil, although their effectiveness is lessened in water that is very cold or deep.

Total sea pollution by oil is estimated to be evenly divided between natural and manmade sources. Natural oil seepage from the seafloor has always occurred, and created mechanisms are in place to neutralize this oil, including bacteria. Of the man-induced oil pollution, most does not come from accidental spills. Instead, much waste oil from industry and transportation finds its way to the sea. There is now much better control of this pollution problem than in earlier years.

87. Is sea level changing today?

Sea level has certainly varied in the distant past. During the postFlood Ice Age, for example, ocean levels dropped by about 200 feet (61 m). This opened up land bridges and led to the geographic distribution of animals (Question 50).

In modern times sea level has remained very constant with equilibrium between incoming and outgoing water. Global warming enthusiasts have predicted an imminent melting of west Antarctic ice and subsequent rising oceans. This has not yet occurred, as shown by high rise buildings built along shorelines worldwide. The oceans appear to be very stable systems.

88. Why is the Dead Sea so salty?

The Dead Sea or Salt Sea is the most mineral-laden body of water on earth, seven times saltier than the major oceans. It is located at the southern end of the Jordan River Valley, a long "rift" or trough in the earth's crust (Question 99). The Dead Sea surface is 396 meters (1300 feet) below sea level, the lowest depression on earth. The Jordan River flows into the Dead Sea and there is no outlet except by evaporation. This water loss is enhanced by the desert temperature which often exceeds 38°C (100°F) by day. Rain averages only 2 inches per year in this desert region. Chemicals carried into the Dead Sea by the Jordan River have accumulated greatly over the years. These include sodium, potassium, and magnesium chlorides and bromides. Many springs with sulfur and iron also join the river along its course, adding to the chemical load. Deuteronomy 8:9 refers to iron and copper deposits in the surrounding hills of Palestine which gradually leach into the sea. Millions of tons of salt are dissolved in the water and salt crystals grow on the sea bottom. Minerals are mined at the south end of the sea by Israel using solar evaporation ponds.

The Dead Sea measures 4–6 miles wide, 10 miles long (8 by 16 km), and about 1200 feet (366 m) deep at its maximum. The water feels oily to the touch and leaves visible salt on one's skin when it dries. No fish can survive in the Dead Sea but there are a few varieties of hardy creatures such as bacteria and brine shrimp. Unusual salt formations can be found along the Dead Sea shoreline, reminding us of the fate of Lot's wife (Gen. 9:26). Petroleum occasionally floats to the sea surface, revealing additional oil wealth stored beneath the sea.

Bible prophecy of millennial times refers to a river of water that will flow from the rebuilt Jerusalem Temple, toward the Dead Sea. No such stream exists at present. There is also the promise that Dead Sea waters will one day be fresh and productive (Ezek. 47:1–12; Zech. 14:8). This may refer to the location where the future river enters the sea, called an *estuary* (see Question 89). The future river may also overflow the salty sea, causing a layer of fresh water that could float above the brine. Dead Sea water today is so dense that it is quite calm and dense, while fresh water is lighter in weight.

There are former shorelines above the current Dead Sea boundary that show the water was once twice as deep as today. The level of the Dead Sea is currently dropping further, about 28 inches (70 cm) per year. There is thus room for a great millennial expansion of this unique sea. Israeli engineers may also increase the size of the Dead Sea in future years. Under consideration is an aqueduct which would carry water from the Mediterranean to the Dead Sea. This 1300-foot drop in water elevation could be used to generate large amounts of hydroelectricity. Since the Mediterranean water is less salty, this project would begin a process of diluting and freshening the Dead Sea. For similar reasons, Jordan had also considered building a canal from the Gulf of Aqaba to the south end of the Dead Sea. The Dead Sea appears to have an interesting future (Frumkin and Elitzur, 2001).

89. What is an estuary?

This is a coastal area where the shoreline has been eroded or submerged, or else the surrounding sea level has risen. Estuaries also include a river which flows into the sea. The result is a large river mouth, usually funnel-shaped. Estuaries are common coastline features. Examples along the U.S. Atlantic east coast include the Chesapeake and Delaware Bays. The word *estuary* comes from the Latin for tide or surge.

Estuaries experience a daily tidal mixing of fresh and salt water. This brackish water may extend far inland as an arm of the sea. The quiet, protected environment encourages an unusually rich diversity of life. Plants, birds, and aquatic life flourish in estuaries, particularly the larval forms of many species.

Chapter Six
Further Questions from the Bible and Geology

90. Was there a pre-Adam race?

This question is closely tied to the gap theory interpretation of Genesis. It proposes that an entire civilization lived on the earth before Adam and Eve were created. This former "pre-Adamic" world also fell into sin and was destroyed. Satan and his host of fallen angels are said to come from this former era of history. In this view the original creation is briefly described in Genesis 1:1, with all the rest of Scripture applying to the present, reorganized creation of mankind. An unspecified time interval is inserted between Genesis 1:1 and 1:2, perhaps billions of years. Thus the long ages of naturalistic geology are accommodated. However, there are several serious problems with the theory of a pre-Adamic world:

• A Scriptural basis is lacking.

> Genesis 1:2 says the earth *was* without form originally, not that it *became* without form after destruction of a supposed earlier civilization. The "without form and void" of Genesis 1:2 does not suggest an earlier time of evil or judgment, but only implies an initial creation which was yet unformed and unfinished (Fields, 1976).

> Romans 5:12 indicates that there was no death before the Fall of Genesis 3. The gap theory pictures early sin, judgment, and death in a world that is claimed by God to be very good.

> 2 Peter 3: 5–7 makes no reference to a former world as it surveys earth history. Nor is an earlier creation described or hinted at elsewhere in Scripture.

• The gap theory holds that the sedimentary rock layers, fossils, and "early man" finds are from the pre-Adamic world. This view reduces the Genesis Flood to an insignificant later event without physical evidence in the world today.

• The gap theory is an attempt to account for the large blocks of time demanded by secular science. As declared throughout this book, however, such a compromise is completely unnecessary. A long time scale for the earth is not essential.

91. Were the days of Creation literal?

There have been many attempts to interpret the Genesis days variously as long ages, as normal days separated by large time gaps, or as non-literal poetic language. However, all such attempts "short change" both scripture and science. The creation account most naturally describes literal, twenty-four hour days for the following reasons:

• Early readers of Genesis understood the creation days as literal. The non-literal theories are almost all of modern origin and are artificial at best. The initial intent and understanding of scripture are key factors in interpreting the Bible. And if the days are not literal, the various modern interpretations become hopelessly confusing and contradicting of each other.

• The descriptive pattern of evening and morning in Genesis 1 pictures literal days. Whenever these terms are used with the adjectives first day, second day, etc in scripture, the literal meaning of day is intended. It is true that the word *day* has multiple uses in Scripture, but so does virtually every word in our languages today. Context is needed, and the creation days clearly are defined in Genesis 1:5 as literal.

• One day with the Lord is like a thousand years according to 2 Peter 3:8. God is therefore above time and not controlled by it. Creation details may appear to us to require a long time period, but could actually occur quickly, if not instantaneously.

• Exodus 20:11 explains that the creation days are a pattern for our present calendar week. There is no astronomical basis for the 7-day week, as is the case for the day (one earth rotation) or the year (one earth revolution). The weekly cycle that we live by thus was given to us directly by the Creator. God could have created all things in either six microseconds or over six trillion years, but clearly chose six days as a pattern for us.

- Some have tried to place a gap of indeterminate time between the first two verses of Genesis. This is an unnecessary attempt to explain the fossil record as resulting from a former inhabited world. However there is no biblical or scientific evidence for an earlier world with a "pre-Adamic" race (see Question 90).
- The Genesis account of origins is not written in poetic, nonliteral form. Instead it is a historical narrative and is meant to be taken literally. There *is* poetry in scripture, such as Genesis 2:23, but not the creation details of Genesis 1 and 2.
- A vast age for the earth inevitably faces a conflict in explaining our first parents. Either God breathed his spirit into already-existing apes, contradicting Matthew 19:4, Luke 1:70, and 2 Corinthians 15:39, or else he re-entered a mature world to create Adam and Eve, contradicting the narrative flow of Genesis 1 and 2.
- It is illogical to believe that mankind is the capstone of creation, then to allow for billions of preceding years of purposeless slow earth changes, evolution, blind alleys, disease, predation, and animal extinction. In this way, mankind is placed as a "tag end" afterthought, following 99.9 percent of earth history.
- Biblical chronology in Genesis 5 and 10 places a limitation on the age of mankind. Thousands of years are allowed; millions or billions of years are not.
- According to Romans 5:12, death first entered the earth at the time of the curse. At the end of the creation week, the earth is declared pure and "very good" (Genesis 1:31). Therefore, many generations of animal death before the fall of Adam and Eve lead to serious theological conflicts. Some attempt to limit Romans 5:12 to spiritual death rather than physical, and also to exclude animal death. This view fails to recognize the universality of Romans 5:12 death, as amplified in Genesis 3:19,21 and Romans 8:19–22.
- The creation was a series of supernatural, instantaneous acts spread over six days. For example, Psalm 33:9 explains that

God spoke and the world came to be; He commanded, and it instantly stood firm. Similarly, Jesus' New Testament miracles were also supernatural and instantaneous.

- The fossils and sedimentary layers of the earth are a result of the Genesis Flood, not long ages of slow accumulation. If the rock layers somehow formed slowly over vast ages, then the Flood becomes an insignificant event with no visible evidence.

- Science data does not *require* vast ages of time for earth's history. There are many evidences that point to a recently created earth, only about ten thousand years old or less. Why dilute the miracle of creation with a vast time scale when there is no need?

- Most long age views for the universe assume that a big bang theory was the initial event, occurring 8–16 billion years ago. However, this compromise fails on two accounts. First, the big bang is a theory riddled with weaknesses, inconsistencies, and "missing links" (DeYoung, 2000) Second, Genesis gives an entirely different sequence of events than predicted by the big bang theory.

- Two major reasons for extending the days of creation are to allow for radioisotope dating results, and also to explain how we can see faraway galaxies. Radioisotope results are evaluated in Question 26. For vast space distances, consider 2 Peter 3:10–11. This passage describes a rapid, supernatural, future reprogramming of the cosmos. It will take place quickly from the vantage point of the earth, just as the initial creation is described. That is, God can cause the light from faraway stars to reach the earth instantly.

This list of evidences in favor of a literal six-day creation could be continued almost indefinitely. Belief in 24-hour creation days and a young earth are not salvation issues. However, they definitely are a measure of consistent Bible interpretation, as well as a measure of one's view of God's creation and control over his universe.

92. How has the curse affected geology?

The curse recorded in Genesis 3 affected mankind, the earth, and the entire universe beyond. This *Fall* of our first parents, Adam and Eve, brought sin, suffering, and death to the earth. The curse also is closely connected with the universal second law of thermodynamics. The first law states that energy is conserved or constant in any physical process. Energy conservation ensures a dependable, predictable universe. The second law, however, is the more dissonant idea that energy becomes unavailable in any transfer process. Alternately, the second law says that all things gradually becomes disordered and wear out. Death itself is an ultimate consequence of this universal law of decay. The first and second laws of thermodynamics are two of the most basic rules of nature.

In geology, a general term for deterioration is called *weathering*. As rocks weather they dissolve or disintegrate into smaller fragments. Likewise, entire mountains erode and wear downward. In some way, the original creation evidently was made perfect without the universal downward direction of aging, erosion, or weathering processes. Perhaps restorative mechanisms were in place. At the *Fall*, however, the ground became cursed and began to produce thorns and thistles (Gen. 3:17–18). The soil evidently became less healthy and productive than previously. Romans 9: 20–22 further describes fallen nature as decaying or "groaning."

Since the cursed world is our only experience, it is difficult to envision a perfect world without death and decay. However, those who personally know and trust in the Creator will enjoy a perfect world someday. Meanwhile, the temporary nature of things in this world was well described by the English poet Percy Bysshe Shelley (1792–1822). His poem *Ozymandias* describes the scattered remains from the reign of the great Ramses II in ancient Egypt (Figure 6-1). This Ramses may have been the Pharaoh at the time of the Egyptian plagues (Ex. 7–11):

I met a traveler from an antique land
Who said: Two vast and trunkless legs of stone

Figure 6-1. From a photo of Ramses II ruins from Luxor, Egypt. There is a modern museum at the site. Additional photos are at http://www.geocities.com/Athens/Aegean/2507/egypt/ram1.jpg.

> Stand in the desert, Near them, on the sand,
> Half sunk, a shattered visage lies, whose frown,
> And wrinkled lip, and sneer of cold command,
> Tell that its sculptor well those passions read
> Which yet survived (stamped on these lifeless things),
> The hand that mocked them and the heart that fed.
> And on the pedestal these words appear:
> "My name is Ozymandias, king of kings;
> Look on my works, ye Mighty, and despair!"
> Nothing beside remains. Round the decay
> Of that colossal wreck, boundless and bare
> The lone and level sands stretch far away.

How quickly the great leaders and monuments of this fallen earth return to dust and are forgotten. Likewise, the earth's present mountains and valleys will not exist forever.

93. Which biblical miracles involve water?

Water is the natural resource most mentioned in the Bible. The value of water is readily known across the Middle East region with its desert climate. It is appropriate that the "water of life" is a phrase used to describe the gospel (Rev. 22:17). Not all of the Bible miracles involve water but many do, including the following:

Genesis	6–8	Noahic flood
Exodus	7:19–24	Water turned to blood
	14:21–29	Parting of the Red Sea
	15:23–25	Bitter waters of Marah sweetened
	17:5–6	Water is provided from the rock
Numbers	20:7–11	Moses strikes the rock for water
Joshua	3:14–17	Waters of the Jordan River divided
Judges	6:36–40	Dew on Gideon's fleece
1 Kings	18:41–46	Elijah prays and God sends rain
2 Kings	2:7–8	Elijah parts the Jordan River
	2:19–22	Elisha cleanses the waters at Jericho
	3:15–20	Ditches filled with water
	5:1–14	Naaman healed of leprosy by washing in the Jordan
	6:5–7	An iron axe head floats
Jonah	1:4–16	A storm and a giant fish stop Jonah from fleeing Ninevah
Matthew	17:24–27	Coin from a fish
Luke	5:6	Great catch of fish
	8:22	Storm is calmed
	8:26	Herd of swine drown
John	2:1–11	Water becomes wine
	6:19	Jesus walks on the sea
	21:6	Miraculous catch of fish

Some of these miracles are also described in other books of the Bible. Additional miracles involving water also could be added to this list. Clearly, water plays an important part in all of scripture, including Christ's ministry on earth.

94. Where was the Garden of Eden located?

It is impossible for us to know this location today. The land and seas that existed before the Genesis Flood have been completely rearranged. Both the breaking up of the fountains of the deep (Gen. 7:11) and the upward thrusting of post-Flood mountains (Psalm 104:8) speak of worldwide geologic alteration by tectonic activity. Also an average of a mile depth of sedimentary rock now cover the continents. In 2 Peter 3:6, the preFlood world is described as completely restructured: "By these waters also the world of that time was deluged and destroyed." Noah's ark landed on Mount Ararat, located in

Figure 6-2. A map showing part of the *Fertile Crescent*, including the Tigris and Euphrates Rivers.

what is today Turkey, about 700 miles (1126 km) from modern Israel. How close the ark's construction site was to the original Garden of Eden, and how far the ark drifted during the Flood are not known.

Genesis 2 names four rivers of Eden as well as surrounding lands. Some of these names, the Tigris and Euphrates Rivers for example, are still used today (Figure 6-2). However, the named pre and postFlood rivers are not necessarily the same waterways. Today's rivers and lands probably were given names that Noah and his family remembered from the pre-Flood world.

The Tigris-Euphrates River Valley is often described as the cradle of civilization. In postFlood times this Fertile Crescent region was the home of Abraham and also the location of the ancient Tower of Babel. It is often assumed that the Garden of Eden also was located here, in the area of modern southern Iraq. However, this region is underlain by about 10 km (6 miles) of sedimentary rock, mostly limestone. This is likely

Flood-deposited rock. Clearly the local preFlood geography was obliterated and then deeply buried. Whether or not this region was originally in proximity to the Garden of Eden simply is not known.

95. What earthquakes are described in Scripture?

Several earthquakes are described in Scripture. Some are historical events and others are predictions. The following are brief descriptions of ten biblical earthquakes. See also Question 96.

Genesis 7:11 "All the fountains of the great deep were broken up, and the windows of heaven were opened." This Flood description implies tectonic activity on a worldwide scale.

Exodus 19:18 "Mount Sinai was completely in smoke, because the Lord descended upon it in fire. Its smoke ascended like the smoke from a furnace, and the whole mountain quaked violently." Volcanic activity and an earthquake accompanied the Lord's presence. The Ten Commandments were given at this time.

Numbers 16:31–33 "As he [Moses] finished speaking all these words, the ground split apart under them, and the earth opened its mouth and swallowed them up, with their households and all the men with Korah, and all their possessions. So they and all those with them went down alive into the pit; the earth closed over them, and they perished from among the assembly." Earthquakes do not generally cause fissures to open and swallow people or buildings. However an exception is described in Numbers 16. Korah and 250 of his followers had rebelled against the leadership of Moses and Aaron in the wilderness. This earthquake was predicted by Moses just before it occurred (Numbers 16:30).

1 Samuel 14:15 "And there was trembling in the camp, in the field, and among all the people. The garrison and the raiders also trembled; and the earth quaked, so that it was a very great trembling." At this time the Philistines were defeated in a battle with Israel.

1 Kings 19:11 "After the wind [was] an earthquake, but the Lord was not in the earthquake." This happened when God spoke to Elijah with a "still small voice."

Psalm 104:8 "At the sound of Thy thunder they [floodwaters] hurried away. The mountains rose; the valleys sank down to the place which thou didst establish for them" (NASV; see Question 53). The floodwaters moved from the land to the ocean basins, probably accompanied by global tectonic activity.

Amos 1:1 (Zechariah 14:5) "The words of Amos, who was among the sheepbreeders of Tekoa...he saw...two years before the earthquake." This earthquake is thought to have occurred around 750 BC, and also is recorded in Zechariah 14:5 and in secular literature. The reference has proven useful in dating the book of Amos. This event was one of the strongest earthquakes ever to shake the city of Jerusalem (Austin, et al., 2000).

Matthew 27:51–54 "The earth quaked and the rocks were split, and the graves were opened; and many bodies of the saints who had fallen asleep were raised." This earthquake accompanied the Lord's death on Calvary.

Matthew 28:2 "And behold, there was a great earthquake; for the angel of the Lord descended from heaven, and came and called back the stone from the door and sat on it." This event took place at the Lord's resurrection.

Acts 16:26 "Suddenly there was a great earthquake, so that the foundations of the prison were shaken; and immediately all the doors were opened and everyone's chains were loosed." At this time Paul and Silas were freed from prison.

96. Does a fault line run through the Mount of Olives?

This question follows from the scripture verse Zechariah 14:4,

> And in that day His feet will stand on the Mount of Olives, which faces Jerusalem on the east. And the Mount of Olives shall be split in two, from east to west, making a very large valley. Half of the mountain shall move toward the north and half of it toward the south.

Figure 6-3 illustrates the future separation of the Mount of Olives. This steep hill overlooks the city of Jerusalem. Today the hillside is largely a cemetery with scattered olive trees. The verse describes an event that will occur when the Lord returns to earth. The description fits that of a large-scale *normal* fault, where tension causes a separation of bedrock. There are indeed many fault lines within the Mount of Olives, and several of them could trigger the events described in Zechariah 14:4.

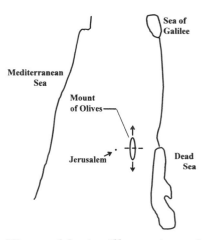

Figure 6-3. An illustration of the future dividing of the Mount of Olives (dotted line), not drawn to scale. The small arrows indicate the predicted direction of separation.

97. What kind of stone was used for the temple in Jerusalem?

Limestone is the main rock type found in the Palestine region. It was often cut into large blocks in quarries and used as building stone. Besides the temple built by Solomon, limestone was also used for the massive walls around the Old City of Jerusalem. Limestone is a sedimentary rock made of calcium carbonate, $CaCO_3$. The rock is sometimes composed of a collection of fused marine shell fragments. Around the world, limestone is still one of the most commonly used and most durable building materials.

When heated, limestone rock is reduced to a useful powder called lime. If water is later added, the slurry becomes plaster. Stucco is a mixture of this plaster and powdered marble chips. Clay and sand mixed with lime makes cement or concrete. Old Testament Hebrews were familiar with all these construction materials. For example, Isaiah 33:12 refers to the burning of lime.

As Jesus' disciples were leaving the rebuilt temple in Jerusalem, one of them remarked,

> Teacher,
> See what manner of stones
> And what buildings are here (Mark 13:1)!

Some of the limestone blocks in this impressive structure measured as large as 3 feet by 6 feet by 24 feet. Similar size blocks still exist today in the ancient walls of the Old City of Jerusalem. A block this size would weigh over 20 tons. Much to the disciples' surprise, Jesus informed them that not one stone would be left standing upon another. The first temple built by Solomon had already been destroyed by Nebuchadnezzer around 587 BC. The Romans also destroyed the rebuilt second New Testament temple, exactly as predicted, in AD 70.

98. Can stones "cry out"?

This question arises from Luke 19:40, when Jesus makes his triumphal entry into Jerusalem, one week before his death. Some Pharisees became irritated by the celebration and told Jesus to hush his cheering followers. Jesus answered, "If these should keep silent, the stones would immediately cry out." This is an ancient figure of speech, similar to the Old Testament verse Habakkuk 2:11, where the stones of a wall are said to cry out against injustice. One is also reminded of Genesis 4:10, when the Lord spoke to Cain, who had just killed his brother Abel. The Lord said, "The voice of your brother's blood cries out to Me from the ground."

The Luke reference teaches that there is a time when Christ *must* be praised. This statement was actually fulfilled at the cross. When people including the Lord's own disciples fell silent, the ground itself shook with an earthquake and rocks were split apart (Matthew 27:51). The one who created the rocks of the earth is shown to have mastery over them. If inanimate objects are commanded to give testimony, they instantly respond.

On an everyday level, earth materials occasionally make actual sounds. For example, walking upon sand grains will sometimes produce sounds variously described like that of an airplane, frog, or a chirping sound. Also, loud sounds from sand dunes have long amazed and terrified people. They sometimes make booming, cannon-like noises. Researchers believe that these sounds arise when layers of moist sand grains slide across each other. In some unknown way, mechanical motion is converted into intense sound vibrations under certain conditions. Some earthquakes are also accompanied by underground rumbles (Question 70).

99. What is the Great Rift Valley?

A *rift valley* may form when adjacent lands pull apart due to great tension (Figure 6-4). The region between the diverging regions may sink downward to form a broad valley called a *graben*, the German word for "ditch. There are many such features across the earth.

The *Great Rift Valley*, also called the *East African Rift*, is the most extensive rift system on the earth's land surface. It extends from Jordan in the Middle East southward through Af-

Rift Valley

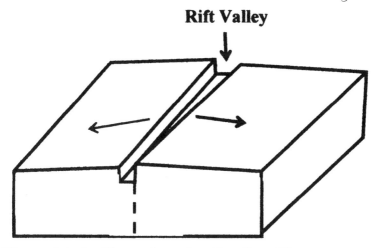

Figure 6-4. An illustration of a rift valley. The center portion collapses or subsides downward as the sides move outward.

rica to Mozambique. Its length totals 4,000 miles (6,400 km), and its width averages 30–40 miles (48–64 km). In the north, the rift occupies the Jordan River valley and the Dead Sea. It provides modern Israel with a valuable farming region. This broad valley also is a major flyway for bird migrations. Each year, a half million white storks travel the corridor between southern Africa and northern Europe. Jeremiah commented that God's people were less faithful and obedient than the migrating storks (Jeremiah 8:7). In the south, a major fossil-hunting area occurs where the Great Rift passes through Ethiopia. It is here where Donald Johanson found the extinct ape fossil called *Lucy* in 1976.

Geologists believe that the Great Rift Valley formed in relatively recent times, accompanied by extensive volcanism along much of its length. This included the formation of such mountains as Kilimanjaro (19,340 feet, 5895 m) and Mount Kenya (17,058 feet, 5199 m). Many creationists believe that the giant rift features resulted from uplift of the land during late stages of the Flood event. Other rift valleys include the Rhine Valley in Germany and the Mid-Atlantic Ridge.

100. What are future changes in geology and geography?

We have limited information on this question. In the long age geologic view, the earth's internal heat will eventually diminish. This would end most volcanic and tectonic activity. The earth's land surface then would gradually wear downward toward sea level. All mountains would eventually disappear.

In the biblical view the Creator will return to earth, perhaps soon, and restore it to its original condition. Whatever form this takes will be a vast improvement on the present. Isaiah 40: 3–4 gives a prophetic description of the Lord's return. The passage may be figurative but it expresses future earth blessings.

> The voice of one crying in the wilderness
> "Prepare the way of the Lord;
> Make straight in the desert
> A highway for our God.

Every valley shall be exalted
And every mountain and hill brought low;
The crooked places shall be made straight
And the rough places smooth."

The future earth will be far different from the present day. The passage indicates that the earth simply will have no features that are physical obstacles or barriers. Even the sun and oceans will not be needed at this time (Rev 21:1,23). There also will be sources of refreshing water where they do not exist today (Question 88). The earth will be ideal in every way including its climate, appearance, and resources. Ezekial 34:26 describes "showers of blessing" which will water the earth. A perfect world simply is impossible for us to comprehend. For all those in God's family, a wonderful future lies ahead.

References

[Questions referenced are shown in brackets.]

Achtemeier, Paul, Editor. 1985. *Harper's Bible Dictionary.* Harper and Row, Publishers, San Francisco. [94]

Austin, Steve, G. Franz, and E. Frost. 2000. Amos's earthquake: an extraordinary Middle East seismic event of 750 B.C. *International Geology Review* 42: 657–671. [95]

Austin, Steve. 1986. Mount St. Helens and catastrophism *Proceedings of the First International Conference on Creationism.* R.E. Walsh, C.L. Brooks, and R.S. Crowell, Editors 1: 3–9. [65]

Austin, Steve. 1994. *Grand Canyon—Monument to Catastrophe.* Institute for Creation Research, Santee, CA. [49]

Austin, Steve, John R. Baumgardner, D. Russell Humphreys, Andrew Snelling, Larry Vardiman, and Kurt P. Wise. 1994. Catastrophic plate tectonics: a global flood model of earth history. *Proceedings of the Third International Conference on Creationism* R.E. Walsh, Editor 609–621. [42]

Austin, Steve, and Mark Strauss. 1999. Are earthquakes signs of the end times? *Christian Research Journal* 21:30–39. [71]

Austin, Steve and Russell Humphreys. 1991. The sea's missing salt: a dilemma for evolutionists. *Proceedings of the Second International Conference on Creationism* R.E. Walsh and C.L. Brook, Editors 2:17–33. [28]

Bates, Gary. 2002. Patriarchs of the forest. *Creation* 25(1):10–13. [27]

Berthault, Guy. 1994. Experiments in statification. *Proceedings of the Third International Conference on Creation* R.E. Walsh, Editor 103–110. [21]

Blount, Kitty and Maggie Crowley, editors. 2001. *Dinosaur Encyclopedia.* Dorling Kindersley Books, New York. [52]

Brown, Walter. 2001. *In the Beginning.* Center for Scientific Creation, Phoenix, AZ. [42]

Buhler, Rich. 1990. Scientists discover hell in Siberia. *Christianity Today* 34(10):28–29. [75]

Chittick, Don. 1997. *The Puzzle of Ancient Man.* Creation Compass, Newberg, OR. [46]

Corliss, William. 1980. Polystrata fossils. *Unknown Earth: A Handbook of Geological Enigmas.* The Sourcebook Project, Glen Arm, MD. [23]

Corliss, William. 1991. *Inner Earth: A Search for Anomalies.* The Sourcebook Project, Glen Arm, MD. [46]

Davies, G. 1981. Migrating nitrogen atoms in diamond. *Nature* 292:288–289. [56]

DeYoung, Don B. 1988. A golden mystery. *Creation Research Society Quarterly* 25(3):153. [57]

DeYoung, Don B. 2000. *Astronomy and the Bible.* Baker Books, Grand Rapids. [91]

DeYoung, Don B. 2000. *Dinosaurs and Creation.* Baker Books, Grand Rapids. [32]

Discovery, www.sonic.net/bristlecone/Schulman.html, July 2002. [27]

Dohan, M. 1981. *Mr. Roosevelt's Steamboat.* Dodd, Mead and Co., New York. [70]

Dorf, Erling. 1964. The petrified forests of Yellowstone Park. *Scientific American* 210(4):106–114. [65]

Eldredge, N. and S. Stanley, Editors. 1984. *Living Fossils.* Springer-Verlag, New York. [11]

Fields, Weston. 1976. *Unformed and Unfilled.* Presbyterian and Reformed Publishing Company, Nutley, NJ. [90]

Flatow, Ira. 1989. *Rainbows, Curve Balls, and Other Wonders of the Natural World Explained.* Harper Collins, New York. [80]

Frumkin, Amos, and Yoel Elitzur. 2001. Rise and fall of the Dead Sea. *Biblical Archaeology Review* 27:43–50. [80]

Gentet, Robert E. 2000. The CCC model and its geologic implications. *Creation Research Society Quarterly* 37(1):10–21. [42]

Gentet, Robert and Edward Lain. 1999. The Nampa Image — an ancient artifact? *Creation Research Society Quarterly* 35(4):203–210. [46]

Gentry, Robert. 1986. *Creation's Tiny Mystery*. Earth Science Associates, Knoxville, TN. [24]

Gidwitz, Tom. 2001. Telling time. *Archaeology* 54(2):36–41. [27]

Hoffman, Paul, and Daniel Schrag. 2000. Snowball earth. *Scientific American* 282(1):68–75. [33]

Holroyd III, Edmond. 1990. An introduction to the possible role of cavitation in the erosion of water channels. *Creation Research Society Quarterly* 27(1):23–32. [41]

Hoover, Richard. 1979. Those marvelous, myriad diatoms. *National Geographic* 155(6):871–878. [10]

Humphreys, D. Russell. 2002. The earth's magnetic field is still losing energy. *Creation Research Society Quarterly* 39: 3–13. [31]

Josephus, Flavius. 1883. *Antiquities of the Jews*, I, in the *Works of Flavius Josephus*. Translated by William Whiston. J. Grigg, Philadelphia. [45]

Kessel, Richard G. and C.Y. Shih. 1976. Scanning electron microscopy in biology, In *A Student's Atlas on Biological Organization* Springer-Verlag, New York. [10]

Kroeber, T. 1961. *Ishi in Two Worlds*. University of California Press, Berkeley, CA. [35]

Lange, Karen. 2002. The evolution of dogs. *National Geographic Magazine* 201(1):2–11. [44]

Millard, Alan. 2002. King Solomon in his ancient context. *Bible and Spade* 15(3):67–80. [57]

Oard, Michael. 1990. *An ice age caused by the Genesis Flood*. Institute for Creation Research, El Cajon, CA. [51]

Oard, Michael. 1999. Paradox of Pacific guyots. *Creation Ex Nihlo Technical Journal* 13(1):1–2. [29]

Oard, Michael. 2000. The extinction of the woolly mammoth: was it a quick freeze? *CEN Technical Journal* 14(3): 24–34. [52]

Oard, Michael. 2001. Vertical tectonics and the drainage of floodwater—a model for the middle and late diluvian period, Parts I, II. *CRSQ* 38(1):3–17; 38(2):79–95. [72]

Oard, Michael. 2002. The mountains rose, a Review of *The Origins of Mountains*. *Technical Journal* 16(3):40–43. [73]

Oard, Michael. 2002. Is catastrophic plate tectonics a part of earth history? *Technical Journal* 16(1):64–68. [42]

Perkins, Sid. 2000. The making of a Grand Canyon. *Science News* 158(14):218–220. [47]

Peterson, Dennis. 2002. *Unlocking the Mysteries of Creation*. Master Books, Green Forest, AR. [46]

Pierce, Larry. 2000. Niagara Falls and the Bible. *Creation* 22: 8–13. [66]

Plummer, Charles, David McGeary, and Diane Carlson. 2003. *Physical Geology*. McGraw-Hill, New York. [18, 64]

Pritchard, James, Editor. 1958. *The Ancient Near East*. Princeton University Press, Princeton, NJ. [38]

Reed, John, Editor. 2000. *Plate Tectonics: A Different View*. Creation Research Society Books, St. Joseph, MO. [72]

Ross, M. 1981. The ice layer in Uranus and Neptune—diamonds in the sky? *Nature* 292:435–436. [17]

Russel, K.M. 1976. Workers find whale in diatomaceaus earth quarry. *Chemical and Engineering News* 54(41):48. [23]

Ryan, William, and Walter Pitman. 1998. *Noah's Flood*. Simon and Schuster, New York. [39]

Salter, Christopher, and Joseph Hobbs, 2003. *World Regional Geography*. Brooks/Cole Publishing, Pacific Grove, CA. [36]

Snelling, Andrew. 1995. Instant petrified wood. *Creation Ex Nihilo* 17(4):38–40. [7]

Snelling, Andrew. 2000. Radiohalos. In *Radioisotopes*. Institute for Creation Research, El Cajon, CA. [25]

Thenius, Erich. 1973. *Fossils and the Life of the Past*. Springer-Verlag, New York. [12]

Vines, Gail. 1999. Inside science: mass extinctions. *New Scientist* 62:1–4. [11]

Weiss, Peter. 2001. Shrimps spew bubbles as hot as the sun. *Science News* 160:213. [41]

Westing, Arthur. 1981. A note on how many humans that have ever lived. *Bioscience* 31(7):523–524. [36]

Wheeler, G. 1975. *The Two-tailed Dinosaur: Why Science and religion conflict over the origin of life.* Southern Publishing Assoc., Nashville, TN. [8]

Whitcomb, John C. and Henry M. Morris. 1961. *The Genesis Flood.* The Presbyterian and Reformed Publishing Company, Philadelphia. [37]

Williams, Emmett, Kenneth House, and Richard Herdklotz. 1981. Solution and deposition of calcium carbonate in a laboratory situation IV. *Creation Research Society Quarterly* 17(4):205–208, 226. [30]

Woodmorappe, John. 1996. *Noah's Ark: A Feasibility Study.* Institute for Creation Research, El Cajon, CA. [44]

Further Study

For readers who wish to learn more about creationist geology, the following technical resources are suggested. All can be ordered at contact@creationresearch.org.

The *Creation Research Society Quarterly* contains articles, letters, and book reviews covering geology and other topics.

Austin, Steve. 1984. *Catastrophes in Earth History.*
DeYoung, Don. 2000. *Dinosaurs and Creation.*
Froede, Carl. 1998. *Field Studies in Catastrophic Geology.*
Oard, Michael. 1997. *Ancient Ice Ages or Giant Submarine Landslides.*
Reed, John. 2000. *The North American Midcontinent Rift System.*
Reed, John. 2001. *Plate Tectonics: A Different View.*
Whitcomb, John and Henry Morris. 1961. *The Genesis Flood.*
Woodmorappe, John. 1999. *Studies in Flood Geology.*

Glossary

absolute age: An actual number of years assigned as the age of an object. Compare with relative age.

angular unconformity: An unconformity in which the lower rock strata dips at an angle different from that of the overlying strata.

aquifer: Saturated rock or sediment through which groundwater moves easily.

basalt: A common igneous rock, usually dark in color due to iron and magnesium content. It is fine-grained and usually erupted onto the earth's surface. Basalt makes up most of the ocean floor.

batholith: A large mass of igneous rock thought to have cooled and crystallized underground.

bed: A single layer of sedimentary rock, distinct from layers above and below it.

bedding: An arrangement of layers or parallel beds of rock.

brachiopod: A bivalved invertebrate marine animal. Their shells are the most common fossil found worldwide.

catastrophism: The belief that many major physical features and changes on earth result from sudden widespread catastrophes rather than gradual evolutionary processes.

chalk: A soft, fine-grained limestone ($CaCO_3$) consisting mostly of fossil foraminifera, tiny one-celled marine animals.

chemical weathering: Alteration of a rock or mineral by chemical reactions.

clay: Sediment with particle size less than .004 mm, or .00015 inch.

continental drift: The concept that today's continents were once joined together as a supercontinent called Pangaea. Some propose that another supercontinent, Gondwanaland, existed before Pangea.

creep: The slow movement of rocks and soil down slopes of hills due to gravity.

Cretaceous Period: The third and most recent geology period of the Mesozoic era. Thought to last from about 144 million years ago to 65 million years ago.

crust: The solid, outermost layer of the earth, averaging about 62 miles (100 km) thick. The crust is thicker under the continents, and thinner beneath the oceans.

crystal: An orderly three-dimensional arrangement of atoms in a solid.

daughter isotope: A secondary isotope produced by the radioactive decay of an original parent isotope. For example, potassium-40 changes to argon-40, and carbon-14 to nitrogen-14.

dendrochronology: The counting of tree rings to determine the age of the tree.

diatom: A microscopic one-celled plant with an intricate silica skeleton. Very abundant in fresh and salt water.

diluvianism: The view that fossils and sedimentary strata formed during the Genesis Flood. This was the dominant position in geology during the sixteenth to nineteenth centuries.

disconformity: An unconformity where the rock strata are parallel above and below a boundary of erosion and/or missing strata.

earthquake: A vibration or shaking of the earth produced by the sudden release of energy stored in distorted, underground rock formations.

epicenter: The location on the earth's surface directly above an underground rock displacement which produces an earthquake. The underground location is the earthquake focus.

erratic: An out-of-place boulder that has been transported to a new location by glacial ice.

estuary: An inlet of the sea along a coastline which causes the mouth of a river to be flooded.

evolution: The theory that life began spontaneously on the earth long ago. Over time, living things have changed on a large, macroscopic scale and given rise to completely new forms, including mankind.

fault: A fracture in a rock mass along which movement has occurred to offset the original rock.

fold: The bending of rock layers which were originally horizontal and parallel. The layers may be folded upward, downward, or into complex ribbon-like patterns.

fossil: A preserved record of life from the past. Remains or traces of a plant or animal are usually embedded in sedimentary rock. From the Latin *fossilis*, meaning "dug up."

fossil fuel: General term for *hydrocarbons* including coal, oil, and natural gas.

geo: A prefix meaning *earth* (Greek).

geography: The study of the earth's surface features. Includes relationships between people and the environment, and the impact of human activity.

geologic column: The division of assumed earth history into large blocks of time, separated by distinct layers of sedimentary rock strata.

geology: The scientific study of the earth. Includes rocks and minerals, surface and internal processes, and earth history. *Geo* and *logy* come from Greek roots for earth and word.

glacier: A large, long-lasting accumulation of ice formed by compaction of snow. A glacier slowly moves downhill away from its source, resembling a frozen river.

granite: An igneous rock composed of quartz, feldspar, and biotite minerals. Thought to have cooled and hardened underground.

groundwater: Water below the ground surface, filling crevices and pore spaces within rocks and sediment.

half-life: The time interval needed for 50 percent of remaining radioactive atoms to decay to a daughter product.

homology: Similarities in the structures of organisms, such as the flippers of a seal and the hands of a person.

hydro: A prefix meaning *water* (Greek).

hydrologic cycle: The movement of water from the sea into the atmosphere by evaporation, unto the land by precipitation, and then back again to the sea as runoff.

ice age: A worldwide cold period with accompanying continental glaciation which covers much of the earth's surface.

igneous rock: Rocks formed by the cooling of molten material. Some rocks crystallize underground (granite), and others at the surface (basalt).

index fossil: The fossil of an organism believed to have lived during a narrow, well-defined interval of geologic time.

isostasy: The concept of the earth's crust floating on the more dense, underlying mantle.

isotopes: Particular forms of a chemical element with different atomic masses, such as oxygen 16, 17, and 18. Isotopes differ by the number of neutrons within the atom's central nucleus.

law of superposition: The reasonable assumption that overlying rock layers are younger than those below.

limestone: A sedimentary rock consisting mainly of calcite, $CaCO_3$.

lith: A prefix or suffix meaning stone or rock (Greek).

living fossil: A plant or animal that appears unchanged from "ancient" fossils. Most living fossils were once thought to be long extinct, then were found living in modern times.

magma: Hot, molten underground rock material that may also contain solid crystals and dissolved gases.

mantle: A shell of underground rock, about 2885 km (1789 miles) thick, which separates the earth's crust from the central core. The mantle comprises about 82 percent of the earth's total volume.

marine: Related to sea water and containing dissolved salts.

mechanical weathering: The physical disintegration of a rock or mineral into smaller fragments. The process is often aided by the freeze-thaw cycle of water.

metamorphic rock: Rock that has been modified by heat, pressure, or chemicals. Includes marble which forms from limestone, and slate that was once shale.

meteorite: A rock from space that passes through the atmosphere and strikes the earth's surface.

Mesozoic era: The geologic period after the Paleozoic and before the Cenozoic. The Mesozoic is said to have extended from about 208 to 65 million years ago. Also called the Age of Reptiles.

mid-ocean ridge: A vast undersea mountain range formed at the margin of two rifting (separating) lithospheric plates.

mineral: A naturally occurring, non-living, crystalline solid with a unique chemical structure. Over 1,000 different earth minerals are known.

nonconformity: An unconformity in which older igneous or metamorphic rock is overlain by younger sedimentary strata.

ocean trench: A deep linear depression in the sea floor where the edge of a crustal plate is being pushed (subducted) downward into the mantle.

orogenesis: The process of mountain formation. From the Greek roots *oros* (mountain) and *genesis* (to come into being).

paleo: A prefix meaning past or ancient (Greek).

paleomagnetism: The study of past earth magnetism as recorded in rocks.

paleontology: The scientific study of plant and animal life from the past, including fossils. Paleontology is often considered a branch of geology.

Pangaea (Pangea): The proposed supercontinent that existed when all the continents were joined into one land mass. Thought by some geologists to have divided 200 million years ago into the northern and southern continents *Laurasia* and *Gondwanaland,* and still later into the present land masses.

parent isotope: A radioactive isotope, such as potassium-40, which eventually decays into a daughter isotope.

petrification: Conversion of organic matter into a hard mineral such as calcite or quartz. The word means "turned into stone."

plate tectonics: The principle that the earth's crust is divided into large, rigid plates which float upon the lower mantle. Movement along the plate margins causes earthquakes and volcanoes.

polystrate fossil: Such fossils extend through two or more distinct sedimentary layers. Some tree fossils extend through multiple layers, and are a testimony to rapid, catastrophic burial.

radioactive decay: The spontaneous process in which an atomic nucleus emits excess neutrons, protons, or energy. The radioactive atom may turn into a different element.

radiohalo: A micron-size region of defects in a crystalline rock due to radioactive decay.

radioisotope dating: Measuring amounts of atomic isotopes in rocks or other objects, and then assuming that this data gives the sample age.

relative age: The sequence in which events took place, without stating an actual number of years. Compare with absolute age.

rock: A solid combination of one or more minerals.

rock cycle: A sequence of processes by which one type of rock is transformed to another type. It may involve rock weathering, metamorphism, or melting.

sedimentary rock: Rock layers formed when sediment settles in water, then later hardens. Most fossils are found in sedimentary rock.

seismology: The study of earthquakes.

tectonics: Large-scale structures, forces, and deformation of the earth's crust.

tsunami: A large, destructive ocean wave produced by an undersea earthquake. Also called a seismic sea wave.

unconformity : An interface between rock strata where erosion or nondeposition has occurred.

uniformitarianism: The view that geological and biological changes in the past always occurred at the slow rates often measured today. Often connected with the denial of supernatural intervention in history.

volcano: A hill or mountain which results from lava or rock fragments ejected from a vent.

water table: The upper surface of underground saturated rock or soil. Groundwater exists beneath the water table.

weathering: The wearing away of rock by the processes of dissolving or disintegration. Weathering results from exposure to water, wind, and atmospheric gases.

Scripture Index

Name Index

Subject Index

Other books available from
Creation Research Society Books
6801 N. Hwy 89, Chino Valley, AZ 86323-9186

Science and Creation, by Wayne Frair, Ph.D.

Scientific Studies in Special Creation, edited by Walter E. Lammerts, Ph.D.

Speak to the Earth, edited by George F. Howe, Ph. D.

Thermodynamics and the Development of Order, edited by Emmett L. Williams, Ph.D.

Did Charles Darwin Become a Christian?, by Wilbert H. Rusch, Sr., M.S., LL.D. and John W. Klotz, Ph.D.

Creationist Research (1964–1980), by Duane T. Gish, Ph.D.

Vestigial Organs Are Fully Functional by Jerry Bergman, Ph.D. and George F. Howe, Ph.D.

Origins: What Is at Stake?, by Wilbert H. Rusch, Sr., M.S., LLD.

Astronomy and Creation, by Donald B. DeYoung, Ph.D.

Ancient Ice Ages or Gigantic Submarine Landslides?, by Michael J. Oard, M.S.

Physical Science and Creation, by Donald B. DeYoung, Ph.D.

Designs and Origins in Astronomy, edited by George Mulfinger, M.S.

Designs and Origins in Astronomy, Volume 2, edited by Donald B. DeYoung, Ph.D., and Emmett L. Williams, Ph.D.

Field Studies in Catastrophic Geology, by Carl R. Froede, Jr., P.G.

The North American Midcontinent Rift System, by John K. Reed, Ph.D.

The Human Body: An Intelligent Design, by Alan L. Gillen, Ed.D., Frank J. Sherwin III, M.A., and Alan Knowles, M.S.

Plate Tectonics: A Different View, edited by John K. Reed, Ph.D.

Natural History in the Christian Worldview, by John K. Reed, Ph.D.

For more information about the
Creation Research Society
and a subscription to the
Creation Research Society Quarterly
write: Membership Secretary
Creation Research Society
P.O. Box 8263
St. Joseph, MO 64508-8263